EMPLOYEE'S RECEIPT

I acknowledge receipt of J. J. Keller's OSHA Safety Training Handbook, which covers 25 different safety topics. These topics include:

An Introduction to OSHA
Company Vehicle Safety
Confined Space Entry (1910.146)

Electrical Safety (1910.301 - .399)
Emergency Response (1910.38, .120)
Eye Protection (1910.132, .133)
Fall Protection (1910.29, .30, and .140)
Fire Prevention (1910.139, .155 - .165)
First Aid and Bloodborne Pathogens (1910.151, .1030)
Foot Protection (1910.132, .136)
Forklift Safety (1910.178)
Hand Protection (1910.132, .138)
Hazard Communication (1910.1200)
Head Protection (1910.132, .135)
Hearing Conservation (1910.95)
Lifting and Ergonomics
Lockout/Tagout (1910.147)
Machine Guarding (1910.212)
Materials Handling Equipment (1910.176 - .184)
Respiratory Protection (1910.132, .134)
Slips, Trips and Falls (1910.21 - 30, .140)
Tool Safety (1910.212, .241 - .244)
Violence in the Workplace
Welding, Cutting, and Brazing (1910.251 - .255)
Workplace Security

_____   _____
Employee's Signature   Date

_____
Company

_____
Company Supervisor's Signature

NOTE: This receipt shall be read and signed by the employee. A responsible company supervisor shall countersign the receipt and place it in the employee's training file.

REMOVABLE PAGE - PULL SLOWLY FROM TOP RIGHT CORNER

J. J. Keller's

OSHA
Safety
Training
Handbook

8th Edition

Copyright 2020

J. J. Keller & Associates, Inc.
3003 Breezewood Lane, P.O. Box 368
Neenah, Wisconsin 54957-0368
Phone: (800) 327-6868
(800) 727-7516
JJKeller.com
Library of Congress Catalog Card Number: 2017932945
ISBN: 978-1-68008-535-8
Canadian Goods and Services Tax (GST)
Number: R123-317687

Printed in the U.S.A.

Eighth Edition

TABLE OF CONTENTS

Introduction to the Worker

Your employer cares about your safety. J. J. Keller's *OSHA Safety Training Handbook* is just part of the effort to teach you about the hazards you face on the job every day. This handbook will be part of the overall safety program your organization has set up to train and protect its workers.

Occupational Safety and Health Administration (OSHA) regulations often require training on particular topics, such as occupational noise exposure or personal protective equipment (PPE). This handbook covers topics important to your safety and health on the job, including subjects like hazard communication and fire prevention. It serves as an aid to your supervisor or instructor in training you on your facility's safety procedures. You need to learn what to do to be safe at work, and your employer needs to teach you what to do. This handbook helps your employer teach you about many topics vital to workplace safety and health.

OSHA regulations for general industry have been issued in the *Code of Federal Regulations*, Title 29, Part 1910. Individual regulations will be identified throughout the handbook as 29 CFR 1910.(section number).

A different set of rules applies if you are doing "construction work." These rules are found in Title 29, Part 1926. The term "construction work" means work for construction, alteration, and/or repair, including painting and decorating. That means your employer doesn't need to be a construction company to sometimes fall under OSHA's construction rules. This book only focuses on OSHA's regulations for general industry.

This book is yours to keep. Use it to follow along with your instructor during training sessions, then keep it to use as a handy reference after you finish your safety training program. You can look up safety and health facts and answer safety questions that occur while you're working. The handbook can be kept in your locker or toolbox to keep safety information at hand whenever you need it.

Together with your employer, you can make every workday a safe one by following the guidelines in J. J. Keller's *OSHA Safety Training Handbook*.

AN INTRODUCTION TO OSHA

More than 90 million Americans spend their days on the job. Yet, until 1970, no law existed to protect workers against workplace safety and health hazards.

In 1970, Congress considered annual numbers such as these:

- Job-related accidents accounted for more than 14,000 worker deaths.

- Nearly 2-1/2 million workers were disabled.

- Estimated new cases of occupational diseases totaled 300,000.

The Occupational Safety and Health Act (OSH Act) of 1970 was passed by a bipartisan Congress "...to assure so far as possible every working man and woman in the nation safe and healthful working conditions and to preserve our human resources."

Why Is OSHA Important to You?

OSHA stands for the Occupational Safety and Health Administration, an agency of the U.S. Department of Labor. The mission of OSHA is to assure safe and healthful working conditions for working men and women by setting and enforcing standards and by providing training, outreach, education, and assistance.

Some of the things OSHA does to carry out its mission are:

- Developing job safety and health standards and enforcing them through worksite inspections.

- Providing training programs to increase knowledge about occupational safety and health.

Since OSHA has been on the job, worker deaths in America are down on average, from about 38 worker deaths a day in 1970 to about 12 a day. Worker injuries and illnesses are down from 10.9 incidents per 100 workers in 1972 to about 3.0 per 100.

What Rights Do You Have Under OSHA?

You have the right to:

- A safe and healthful workplace.

- Know about hazardous chemicals. Employers must have a written, complete hazard communication program that includes information on: container labeling, safety data sheets (SDSs), and worker training. The training must include the physical and health hazards of the chemicals and how workers can protect themselves.

- Report injury or illness to your employer. Your employer may not retaliate or discriminate against a worker for reporting an injury or illness. Employers are required to keep a log of injuries and illnesses. You have a right to see the annual summary of the log.

- Complain or request hazard correction from your employer. OSHA rules protect workers who raise concerns to their employer or OSHA about unsafe or unhealthful conditions in the workplace.

- Training in a language and vocabulary that you can understand. Some required training covers topics that are in this book.

- See and copy hazard exposure and medical records related to your exposure to harmful toxic substances (chemicals) and harmful physical agents (such as noise, heat, cold, vibration, repetitive motion, and ionizing and non-ionizing radiation).

- File a confidential complaint with OSHA if you believe a violation of a safety or health standard, or an imminent danger situation, exists in the workplace. However, often the best and fastest way to get a hazard corrected is to notify your employer.

- Participate in an OSHA inspection. An employee representative can accompany the OSHA inspector, and workers can talk to the inspector privately. Workers may point out hazards; describe injuries, illnesses, or near misses that resulted from those hazards; and describe any concern they have about a safety or health issue. Workers can find out about inspection results and abatement measures, and they may object to dates set for violations to be corrected.

- See any OSHA citations issued to your employer.

- Be free from punishment for exercising safety and health rights. Workers have 30 days to contact OSHA if they feel they have been punished for exercising their safety and health rights.

You can see the list of your rights on the OSHA poster your employer must show in the workplace.

What Responsibilities Does Your Employer Have Under OSHA?

Employers must:

- Provide employees a workplace free from recognized hazards.

- Provide required training to all workers in a language and vocabulary they can understand.

- Keep injury and illness records, and report to OSHA all work-related fatalities within 8 hours and all inpatient hospitalizations, amputations, and losses of an eye within 24 hours. An annual summary of injuries and illnesses must be posted Feb. 1 to April 30.

- Provide required medical exams.

- Not discriminate against workers for exercising their rights. It is illegal to retaliate against an employee for using any of their rights under the law, including raising a health and safety concern with the employer or with OSHA, or reporting a work-related injury or illness.

- Comply with all applicable OSHA standards.

- Prominently display the OSHA poster in the workplace and post OSHA citations at or near the place of the alleged violations.

- Provide and pay for most personal protective equipment (PPE).

What Are OSHA Standards?

OSHA standards are rules that describe the methods employers must use to protect employees from hazards.

Where there are no specific standards, employers must comply with the General Duty Clause of the OSH Act. It states that employers shall furnish to each of his employees employment and a place of employment which are free from recognized hazards that are causing or are likely to cause death or serious physical harm to his employees.

OSHA standards:

- Limit the amount of hazardous chemicals, substances, or noise that workers can be exposed to.

- Require the use of certain safe work practices and equipment.

- Require employers to monitor certain hazards and keep records of workplace injuries and illnesses.

Some of the most frequently cited standards include those for:

- Fall protection.

- Hazard communication.

- Scaffolding.

- Respiratory protection.

- Electrical.

- Powered industrial trucks.

- Ladders.

OSHA

How Are OSHA Inspections Conducted?

The OSH Act authorizes OSHA compliance safety and health officers (CSHOs) to conduct workplace inspections at reasonable times. OSHA conducts inspections without advance notice, except in rare circumstances, such as imminent danger. In fact, anyone who tells an employer about an OSHA inspection in advance can receive fines and a jail term.

There are several different types of OSHA inspections:

*   Imminent danger.

*   Fatality or hospitalizations.

*   Worker complaints/referrals.

*   Targeted inspections — Local Emphasis Program (LEP), National Emphasis Program (NEP), or particular hazards or industries.

*   Follow-up Inspections.

After an OSHA inspection, an employer can be cited for violations of OSHA standards. There are four types of violations:

*   Willful — A violation that the employer intentionally and knowingly commits or a violation that the employer commits with plain indifference to the law.

*   Serious — A violation where there is substantial probability that death or serious physical harm could result and that the employer knew, or should have known, of the hazard.

*   Other-than-serious — A violation that has a direct relationship to safety and health, but probably would not cause death or serious physical harm.

*   Repeated — A violation that is the same or similar to a previous violation.

Where Can You Go for Help?

Employees can get help with safety and health concerns from many sources such as:

- The employer or supervisor, coworkers, and union representatives.

- SDSs for information on chemicals.

- Labels and warning signs.

- Employee orientation manuals or other training materials.

- Procedures and instructions for work tasks.

Outside of the workplace, employees can get help from:

- OSHA's website: http:// www.osha.gov and OSHA offices.

- Compliance Assistance Specialists in the OSHA area offices.

- The National Institute for Occupational Safety and Health (NIOSH) — OSHA's sister agency.

- OSHA Training Institute Education Centers.

- Doctors, nurses, and other health care providers.

- Public libraries.

- Other local, community-based resources.

To file an OSHA complaint, an employee can:

- Download the OSHA complaint form from OSHA's website. Complete the form — be specific and include appropriate details.

- File the complaint online.

- Telephone or visit local OSHA regional or area offices to discuss the concerns.

Workers do not have to reveal their name when they file a complaint. OSHA determines if an inspection is necessary.

Work at Working Safely

As you work, remember:

- The importance of OSHA, including the history of safety and health regulation leading to the creation of OSHA and OSHA's mission.

- Worker rights under OSHA.

- Employer responsibilities.

- OSHA standards.

- OSHA inspections.

- Safety and health resources, including how to file a complaint.

NOTES

Employee _____

Instructor _____

Date _____

Location _____

AN INTRODUCTION TO OSHA REVIEW

1. In addition to setting and enforcing rules, OSHA also:
   a. Approves safety products.
   b. Installs safety alarms.
   c. Provides training.
   d. All of the above.

2. After OSHA was established, the number of injuries and illnesses:
   a. Decreased.
   b. Stayed the same.
   c. Increased.
   d. Decreased only for large employers.

3. The written hazard communication program must include information on:
   a. Emergency evacuation procedures.
   b. Container labeling, SDSs, and training.
   c. Injury and illness records.
   d. Sources of hazardous energy.

4. You cannot get into trouble with your employer if you:
   a. Refuse to wear your PPE.
   b. Remove machine guards.
   c. Report an illness or injury.
   d. Hide damaged tools.

5. If you tell your employer about unsafe conditions:
   a. You will have to join the safety committee.
   b. OSHA rules protect you from getting into trouble with your employer.
   c. You must also eliminate the hazard.
   d. You will be fired.

6. You have the right to:
    a. File a confidential complaint with OSHA.
    b. Talk to the OSHA inspector during an inspection.
    c. See OSHA citations issued to your employer.
    d. All of the above.

7. Your employer must post all of the following, except:
    a. The names of injured employees.
    b. The OSHA poster.
    c. The annual summary of injuries and illnesses.
    d. OSHA citations for violations.

8. Who is responsible for providing and paying for most PPE?
    a. OSHA.
    b. The employee.
    c. The employer.
    d. The safety manager.

9. OSHA inspections can be triggered by:
    a. Fatalities or hospitalizations.
    b. Worker complaints.
    c. National Emphasis Programs.
    d. All of the above.

10. Types of OSHA violations can include all of the following, except:
    a. Serious.
    b. Other-than-serious.
    c. Imminent danger.
    d. Willful.

COMPANY VEHICLE SAFETY

You may be assigned to use a company vehicle to visit clients, make deliveries, attend meetings, pick up supplies, or to do a variety of other tasks. When driving is part of the job, like every other task, it has to be done safely.

Motor vehicle crashes are a leading cause of death, based on data from the National Highway Traffic Safety Administration (NHTSA). Any crash, whether it happens while you're driving a fleet vehicle or during your daily commute, has a big impact on the workplace.

Where Are the Regulations?

The Occupational Safety and Health Administration (OSHA) does not regulate the use of company vehicles, but the agency has issued guidelines for employers to reduce motor vehicle crashes.

OSHA recommends that employers have an effective workplace driver safety program to reduce the risks. The program can:

- Save lives and reduce injuries.
- Protect company resources (people and property).
- Reduce liability risks.

Company Vehicle Safety Program

A company vehicle safety program should include the following 10 steps:

1. Management commitment and employee involvement. Management leads, supports, and enforces the program; but employee input is essential for its success.

2. Written policies and procedures. The program may have policies for driver eligibility, vehicle inspection and maintenance programs, seat belt use, reporting collisions and moving violations, restricting alcohol and drug use, etc.

3. Driver agreements. Drivers should sign an agreement that they are aware of, understand, and will follow the vehicle safety policies and procedures.

4. Motor vehicle record checks for each driver. Each driver's motor vehicle record should be periodically checked for license restrictions, moving violations, accidents, etc.

5. Crash reporting and investigation procedures. Drivers should know what to do in case of a collision, regardless of the severity. Investigations should identify what caused the crash and recommend preventive measures.

6. Vehicle selection, maintenance, and inspection procedures. Employers can use vehicle crash test ratings to help select safe vehicles. The manufacturer's recommended vehicle maintenance program should be followed. Vehicles should have regular inspections, and drivers should know how to report defects. Repairs should be made by qualified mechanics.

7. Disciplinary action system for violations of the program's provisions. Under a fair progressive disciplinary program, a driver could lose his or her driving privileges for certain violations.

8. Reward/incentive programs to promote safe driving. Incentive programs can use recognition, prizes, and special privileges to reward safe drivers.

9. Driver training and communication programs. Periodic training can help establish safe driving habits.

10. Regulatory compliance. Vehicles and drivers must comply with all applicable highway safety laws.

Vehicle Inspections

Safe driving starts before you turn the ignition key. Always inspect the vehicle before you start your trip. Make sure:

- The vehicle does not have any visible damage that affects its safe operation.

- The tires are properly inflated (use the vehicle manufacturer's recommendations that are typically noted on a sticker inside the door, glove box, or trunk — the pressures stamped on the tire are not specific to the vehicle). Check the pressure when the tires are cold.

- Tires have sufficient tread depth (tread depth should be at least 1/16 inch).

- The vehicle's fluid levels are correct (oil, brake, transmission, battery, and wiper fluids).

- Belts and hoses are free of blisters, cracks, and cuts.

- The vehicle has plenty of fuel.

- The windshield wipers are in good condition and are functional.

- You are familiar with the location and operation of all the vehicle's controls; and the seat, steering wheel, and mirrors are properly adjusted.

- Headlights, brake lights, turn signals, emergency flashers, and interior lights are working.

- The seat belt is properly adjusted, and it's in good condition.

- The vehicle is equipped with an emergency kit.

- Loose objects are secured so they won't shift during a sudden stop or turn.

Safe Driving Tips

While it's important to understand the company vehicle safety program, as a driver, you have to put safe driving techniques into practice each time you get behind the wheel. The following safe driving strategies are under the driver's control:

- Make sure the vehicle is safe to operate.
- Bring supplies you may need in case of an emergency.
- Wear your seat belt.
- Drive defensively, not aggressively.
- Pay attention to your driving, and avoid distractions.
- Only drive when you're alert and fully awake.
- Never drive under the influence of alcohol, medications, or illegal drugs.

Plan for Emergencies

In case of a breakdown or accident, your first actions should be to move the car to a safe area, remain in the car (if there is no risk of fire or other danger), and call for help.

Some basic provisions to include in an emergency supply kit can include:

- A phone and a list of emergency phone numbers.

- First aid supplies.

- Roadside warning triangles or flares (follow instructions for their safe use).

- A fire extinguisher.

- Water and food.

- Clothing (raincoat; warm clothing, hat, mittens/gloves; comfortable boots/shoes).

- Basic car maintenance tools (a flashlight with fresh batteries; battery jumper cables; a jack, lug nut wrench, and spare tire; water for the radiator; oil; windshield wiper fluid; rags; gloves; etc.).

- Blankets, candles, matches, and extra cash.

Wear Your Seat Belt

Seat belts are the single most effective means of reducing deaths and serious injuries in traffic crashes. Safety belts save thousands of lives and prevent hundreds of thousands of serious injuries each year.

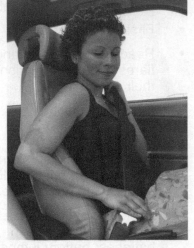

Be Defensive

It's best to always practice defensive driving techniques. Continually check your mirrors, leave enough following distance, and keep a cushion of space around the vehicle in case you need to quickly change lanes or go onto the shoulder.

Aggressive driving acts include:

- Speeding.

- Tailgating.

- Failing to signal lane changes.

- Running red lights or stop signs.

- Passing on the right.

Aside from being aggressive, taking these actions can result in getting a ticket. The best advice is to share the road — allow other drivers to merge as needed. Safely move out of an aggressive driver's way; don't become part of a conflict.

Stay Focused and Alert

Driving is no time to multi-task. Stay focused on the road. Drivers can be distracted by a variety of things:

- Conversations with passengers.

- Eating, drinking, or grooming.

- Tuning the radio.

- Reading maps or directions.

- Using electronic navigation systems.

- Talking or texting on a cell phone.

Cell phones are one type of distraction that is becoming more and more common. Consider NHTSA's policy on using cell phones while driving:

"The primary responsibility of the driver is to operate a motor vehicle safely. The task of driving requires full attention and focus. Cell phone use can distract drivers from this task, risking harm to themselves and others. Therefore, the safest course of action is to refrain from using a cell phone while driving."

Drowsy driving is another problem. At 55 mph, a vehicle travels the length of a football field in 3.7 seconds. This is no time for a nap.

You can take steps to avoid drowsy driving:

- Get a full night of rest before driving.

- Stop and get out of the car to stretch and walk about every two hours.

- Set a realistic goal of how many miles you can safely drive each day.

- Avoid taking medications that cause drowsiness.

The best remedy if you get drowsy behind the wheel is to stop driving and sleep for an extended period. When this isn't practical, studies have found two actions that can make a short-term difference: taking a 20-minute nap (in a safe rest area) and consuming the caffeine equivalent of two cups of coffee. After a nap, the best action is to drive to the closest safe resting spot, such as a motel or home, and sleep for an extended period.

Alcohol, certain prescription drugs and over-the-counter medications, and illegal drugs can all affect a person's ability to drive safely. If you spot an impaired driver, stay a safe distance from the vehicle. Alert the police that there is an unsafe driver on the road.

How do you spot a driver who is under the influence of alcohol? Watch for these driving behaviors:

- Weaving, swerving, drifting, or straddling the center line.
- Driving on the wrong side of the road.
- Driving at very slow or very fast speeds.
- Turning abruptly or braking erratically.
- Responding slowly to traffic signals.
- Driving with headlights off at night.

Work at Working Safely

Driving is a privilege; and as part of your responsibilities:

- Follow the rules in the company vehicle safety program.
- Prepare the vehicle for each trip.
- Plan for emergencies.
- Wear your safety belt.
- Avoid aggressive driving.
- Stay focused and alert while you drive.
- Never drive under the influence of alcohol and drugs, and recognize the warning signs of drivers who do.

Safe at Home

You don't need a formal driving safety program when you're off the clock, but you should follow the same safety tips when you drive your personal vehicle:

- Keep up with regular maintenance so you're sure your vehicle is safe to drive.

- Have a first aid kit, basic maintenance tools, and other emergency supplies ready in case you need them.

- Follow all traffic safety laws, and have adequate insurance.

- Wear your seat belt, and make sure your passengers do the same.

- Stay focused on your driving, and avoid phone calls or other distractions when you drive.

- Don't drive when you're drowsy.

- Never drive if you're under the influence of alcohol or drugs.

NOTES

Employee _____

Instructor _____

Date _____

Location _____

COMPANY VEHICLE SAFETY REVIEW

1. OSHA has issued _____ to reduce work-related motor vehicle crashes.
   a. Standards.
   b. Regulations.
   c. National Emphasis Programs.
   d. Guidelines.

2. In addition to protecting company property and reducing liability risks, a workplace driver safety program can:
   a. Reduce injuries and save lives.
   b. Improve product quality.
   c. Reduce product delivery times.
   d. Increase sales.

3. The first step in a company vehicle safety program is to have:
   a. A fleet of brand new vehicles.
   b. Management commitment and employee involvement.
   c. A team of on-staff mechanics.
   d. Defensive driver training.

4. Under a company disciplinary action system for violations of the company vehicle safety program, a driver could:
   a. Lose his state-issued driver's license.
   b. Have to go to court.
   c. Lose his privileges to drive on the job.
   d. Have to wash all the cars.

5. The company vehicle safety program may have policies for:
   a. Seat belt use.
   b. Vehicle inspection.
   c. Vehicle maintenance.
   d. All of the above.

6. Employers can use vehicle crash test ratings to:
   a. Help select safe vehicles.
   b. Help select safe drivers.
   c. Help select car insurance policies.
   d. All of the above.

7. Each driver's motor vehicle record should:
   a. Never be checked by the employer.
   b. Periodically be checked by the employer.
   c. Be submitted to the local police department.
   d. Be carried in the vehicle.

8. Always inspect the vehicle:
   a. Each time you change the oil.
   b. Every three months.
   c. Before you start your trip.
   d. After something breaks.

9. If you feel drowsy while driving, the best remedy is to:
   a. Stop driving and sleep for an extended period.
   b. Take a quick 5-minute nap.
   c. Eat a big sandwich.
   d. Roll down the window and turn up the radio.

10. A vehicle emergency supply kit can include:
    a. A phone and list of emergency numbers.
    b. First aid supplies.
    c. Water, food, and clothing.
    d. All of the above.

CONFINED SPACE ENTRY

Thousands of workers are exposed to possible death or injury in what are referred to as "confined spaces." The Occupational Safety and Health Administration (OSHA) standard on permit-required confined spaces defines a **confined space** as:

- A space that is large enough for an employee to enter,
- Has restricted means of entry or exit, **and**
- Is not designed for continuous employee occupancy.

A **permit-required confined space** (permit space) is a confined space that presents or has the potential for hazards related to:

- Atmospheric conditions (toxic, flammable, asphyxiating),
- Engulfment,
- Configuration, **or**
- Any other recognized serious hazard.

Where Are the Regulations?

Regulations governing entry to confined spaces are specified by OSHA. You can find these regulations at 29 CFR 1910.146.

Examples of confined spaces include ship compartments, fuel tanks, vats, silos, sewers, tunnels, and vaults. Although these environments are often dangerous, you might have to work in them to inspect, clean, repair, or maintain equipment.

Confined Space Hazards

Let's look further at some of the dangers you might encounter in a permit-required confined space.

Physical Hazards

Physical hazards may result from mechanical equipment or moving parts like agitators, blenders, and stirrers. Dangers may also be present from gases, liquids, or fluids entering the space from connecting pipes. Before entering a permit space, all mechanical equipment must be locked out/ tagged out. All lines containing hazardous materials such as steam, gases, or coolants must also be shut off.

Other physical hazards include heat and excessive noise. Temperatures can build up quickly in a permit space and cause exhaustion or dizziness. Sounds may reverberate and make it hard to hear important directions or warnings.

Oxygen Deficiency

In general, the primary atmospheric hazard associated with permit spaces is oxygen deficiency.

Normal air contains 20.8 percent oxygen by volume. The minimum safe level as indicated by OSHA is 19.5 percent; OSHA defines the maximum safe level as 23.5 percent. A low oxygen level can quickly cause death. Oxygen can be displaced by other gases such as argon, nitrogen, or methane. Oxygen can be consumed by chemical reactions such as rusting, rotting, fermentation, or burning of flammable substances.

Combustibility

Flammable and combustible gases or vapors may be present from previous cargoes, tank coatings, preservatives, and welding gases. These built-up vapors and gases can be ignited by faulty electrical equipment, static electricity, sparks from welding, or cigarettes. The atmosphere is hazardous if tests show the presence of flammable gas, vapor, or mist that is more than 10 percent of its lower flammable limit.

Toxic Air Contaminants

These contaminants occur from material previously stored in the tank or as a result of the use of coatings, cleaning solvents, or preservatives.

Before You Enter

The hazards must be identified before anyone enters a permit-required confined space. A written entry permit must be used for entry into a permit-required confined space. The permit outlines the conditions that make the entry safe. The permit must be posted at the space during an entry, and it must be signed by the entry supervisor.

Control Any Hazardous Energy

Use locks and tags to prevent accidental startup of equipment while you are working in the permit space. Cut off steam, water, gas, or power lines that enter the space.

Test the Air

Use special instruments for testing the levels of oxygen, combustibility, and toxicity in confined spaces.

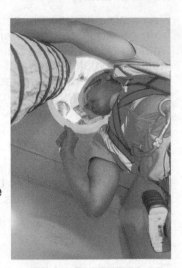

Test before you open the space by probing with test instruments near the entry.

Once the space is opened, test the air from top to bottom. Some gases like propane and butane are heavy, and they will sink to the bottom of the space. Light gases like methane will rise to the top. So you need to be sure to check all levels.

After you are sure that the oxygen level is adequate and there is nothing combustible in the space, test for toxicity. Periodic or continuous follow-up testing may be needed during the entry.

Purge and Ventilate the Space

Some confined spaces may contain water, sediment, hazardous atmospheres, or other unwanted substances. These substances generally must be purged, that is, pumped out or otherwise removed, before entry.

Use ventilating equipment to maintain an oxygen level between 19.5 percent and 23.5 percent. It also should keep toxic gases and vapors to within accepted levels prescribed by OSHA.

Use only safe, grounded, explosion-proof equipment and fans if a combustible atmosphere could develop in the space.

If ventilation does not eliminate the atmospheric hazards, you will need to wear appropriate respiratory protection. You might also need eye and hearing protection and protective clothing.

Rescue Procedures

Almost two-thirds of permit-required confined space deaths result from people attempting a rescue. When workers enter a permit space, at least one person must remain outside to summon help or offer assistance.

When the employer designates this attendant to perform rescue procedures in addition to monitoring the safety of the confined space entrant, he or she should be equipped with the necessary PPE and rescue equipment and trained in first aid and cardiopulmonary resuscitation (CPR). He or she should maintain constant communication with those inside the space. If a situation arises that requires emergency rescue, the attendant must not enter until additional help arrives.

The entrant must wear a full body harness and lifeline so that he or she can be easily pulled from the space. It can be attached to a block and tackle or a winch system that a single rescuer/attendant can operate from outside the space.

The entrant must be trained to recognize hazardous situations so he or she knows when to exit a confined space before a rescue is needed.

Work at Working Safely

You should always follow safe procedures and your company's permit space program. Use the protective equipment provided by your employer. Keep the following safety tips in mind:

1. Use prescribed personal protective and respiratory equipment at all times.

2. Test the air inside the permit space for safe oxygen levels and for flammable, explosive, and toxic vapors and gases before entry. Test periodically while work is in progress.

3. Always use non-sparking tools and explosion proof fans, lights, or air movers when working in permit spaces where there may be a combustible atmosphere.

4. Have trained, well-equipped workers available to rescue anyone who enters a permit space.

If you follow these rules carefully, you will be able to work safely in permit-required confined spaces.

Employee _____

Instructor _____

Date _____

Location _____

CONFINED SPACE ENTRY REVIEW

1. A "confined space" is a space that:
   a. Isn't designed for continuous employee occupancy.
   b. Is large enough for an employee to enter.
   c. Has restricted means of entry or exit.
   d. All of the above.

2. A "permit-required confined space":
   a. Must be a "confined space."
   b. Has hazards within it or has the potential for hazards to develop.
   c. Might need to be entered to do certain jobs.
   d. All of the above.

3. Hazardous moving machine parts in a confined space:
   a. Are a physical hazard.
   b. Cause the space to meet the definition of a "permit-required confined space."
   c. Must be locked out or tagged out before entry.
   d. All of the above.

4. Over time, rusting metal inside of a confined space can lead to:
   a. A strong odor.
   b. A dusty atmosphere.
   c. An oxygen-deficient atmosphere.
   d. Engulfment.

5. The use of coatings or cleaning solvents inside of a permit space:
   a. Can cause a toxic atmosphere.
   b. Is an example of a physical hazard.
   c. Is only safe if the space is locked out.
   d. Will not cause any hazards.

6. When you test the air inside of a permit-required confined space:
   a. Check only the bottom of the space.
   b. Check only at the opening of the space.
   c. Test the air from top to bottom.
   d. Check only at the top of the space.

7. An entry permit is signed by:
   a. OSHA.
   b. The entry supervisor.
   c. The entrants.
   d. The attendant.

8. Test the air first for:
   a. Noise.
   b. Oxygen.
   c. Combustibility.
   d. Toxicity.

9. If ventilation doesn't eliminate the atmospheric hazards in the space:
   a. The entry must be done very quickly.
   b. There must be two teams of attendants outside of the space.
   c. The entrants will need to wear respirators.
   d. None of the above.

10. The entrant wears a full body harness and lifeline so he or she:
    a. Can be quickly pulled from the space in case of an emergency.
    b. Will not get lost.
    c. Can't get close to moving machine parts.
    d. Will not fall down.

ELECTRICAL SAFETY

Electricity is such an integral part of our lives at home and in the workplace that we can tend to take its power for granted. But it's a sobering fact that hundreds of workers are electrocuted each year.

Electrical accidents in the workplace can, for the most part, be avoided if you use safe electrical equipment and work practices.

Where Are the Regulations?

The Occupational Safety and Health Administration (OSHA) has devoted an entire section (Subpart S) of its regulations to rules governing electrical work. These regulations can be found in 29 CFR 1910.301-.399. In addition, you may need to comply with regulations relating to personal protective equipment, found in Subpart I of the General Industry regulations.

Your employer must train you in safe work practices for working with electrical equipment. Section 1910.332 specifically covers training related to your job. The training rules distinguish between workers who work on or near exposed energized parts and those who do not. Even if you are not qualified to work on exposed energized equipment, you must know the specific safety practices which apply to your job.

Are You Qualified to Work With Electricity?

OSHA has designated two categories of workers who face a risk of electric shock that is not reduced to a safe level by using electrical protective devices. These categories identify workers who are:

- **Unqualified**, that is, those workers who face a risk of electric shock, but are not trained to work on or near exposed live parts. Unqualified employees must be trained in and familiar with safety-related work practices required in Subpart S.

- **Qualified**, that is, those workers trained on avoiding the hazards of working on or near exposed live parts, in addition to the training required for unqualified workers. Qualified workers are trained: to distinguish exposed live parts from other parts of electric equipment, in methods to determine nominal voltage of exposed live parts, and to know the proper clearance distances.

This chapter focuses on information needed by workers who are unqualified.

How Does Electricity Work?

To handle electricity safely, including working with electrical equipment, you need to understand how electricity acts, the hazards it presents, and how those hazards can be controlled.

Electricity is the flow of electrons through a conductor. An electron is a tiny particle of matter that orbits around the nucleus of an atom. Electrons of some atoms are easily moved out of their orbits. This ability of electrons to move or flow is the basis of electrical current.

When you activate a switch to turn on an electric machine or tool, you allow current to flow from the generating source through conductors (wires) to the area of demand (motor).

A complete circuit is necessary for the controlled flow of electrons along a conductor. A complete circuit is made up of a source of electricity, a conductor, and a consuming device (load).

Volts = Current × Resistance (or V=IR)

The equation, Volts = Current × Resistance, is known as Ohm's Law. The factors discussed below relate to one another as described by this equation. This relationship makes it possible to change the qualities of an electrical current but keep an equivalent amount of power.

A force or pressure must be present before water will flow through a pipeline. Similarly, electrons flow through a conductor because *electomotive force* (EMF) is exerted. The unit of measure for EMF is the *volt*.

For electrons to move in a particular direction, a potential difference must exist between two points of the EMF source. For example, a battery has positive and negative poles.

The continuous movement of electrons past a given point is known as *current*. It is measured in *amperes*. The movement of electrons along a conductor meets with some opposition. This opposition is known as *resistance*. Resistance to the flow of electricity is measured in *ohms*. The amount of resistance provided by different materials varies widely.

For example, most metals offer little resistance to the passage of electric current. However, porcelain, wood, pottery, and some other substances have a very high resistance to the flow of electricity. In fact, these substances can be used as insulators against the passage of electric current.

What Are the Hazards of Electricity?

The primary hazards of electricity and its use are:

- Shock
- Burns
- Arc-blast
- Explosions
- Fires

Shock

Electric currents travel in closed circuits through some kind of conducting material. You get a shock when some part of your body becomes part of an electric circuit. An electric current enters the body at one point and exits the body at another location. High-voltage shocks can cause serious injury (especially burns) or death.

You will get a shock if a part of your body completes an electrical circuit by:

* Touching a live wire and an electrical ground, or

* Touching a live wire and another wire at a different voltage.

The severity of the shock a person receives depends on several factors:

* How much electric current flows through the body.

* What path the electric current takes through the body.

* How much time elapses while the body is part of the electric circuit.

What happens to the body?

A current as small as 60/1000 of an ampere can kill you if it passes through your chest. The typical household current operates at 15 amperes.

The effects of an electric shock on the body can range from a tingle in the part touching the circuit to immediate cardiac arrest. A severe shock can cause more damage to the body than is readily visible.

Relatively small burn marks may be all that are visible on the outside. However, a severely shocked person can suffer internal bleeding and severe destruction of tissues, muscles, and nerves. Finally, a person receiving an electric shock may suffer broken bones or other injuries that occur from falling after receiving a shock.

The case of water

In its pure state, water is a poor conductor of electricity. However, if even small amounts of impurities are present in the water (salt in perspiration, for example), it becomes a ready electrical conductor.

Therefore, if water is present anywhere in the work environment or on your skin, be extra careful around any source of electricity.

Burns

Burns can result when a person touches electrical wiring or equipment that is improperly used or maintained. Typically, such burn injuries occur on the hands.

Arc-Blast

Arc-blasts occur when high-amperage currents jump from one conductor to another through air, generally during opening or closing circuits, or when static electricity is discharged. Fire may occur if the arcing takes place in an atmosphere that contains an explosive mixture.

Explosions

Explosions occur when electricity provides a source of ignition for an explosive mixture in the atmosphere. Ignition can be due to overheated conductors or equipment, or normal arcing (sparking) at switch contacts. OSHA standards, the National Electrical Code, and related safety standards have precise requirements for electrical systems and equipment used in hazardous atmospheres.

Fires

Electricity is one of the most common causes of fire both in the home and workplace. Defective or misused electrical equipment is a major cause, with high resistance connections being one of the primary sources of ignition. High resistance connections occur where wires are improperly spliced or connected to other components such as receptacle outlets and switches.

High resistance connections cause heat to build up. In some cases, enough heat can build up to start a fire.

Causes of Electrical Accidents

It is important for you to understand how to avoid electrical hazards when you work with electrical power tools, maintain electrical equipment, or install equipment for electrical operation.

Accidents and injuries in working with electricity are caused by one or a combination of the following factors:

- Unsafe equipment and/or installation.

- Unsafe workplaces caused by environmental factors.

- Unsafe work practices.

Preventing Electrical Accidents

Protective methods to control electrical hazards include:

- Insulation.

- Electrical protective devices.

- Guarding.

- Grounding.

- PPE.

Insulation

Insulators of glass, mica, rubber, or plastic are put on electrical conductors to protect you from electrical hazards. Before you begin to work on any piece of electrical equipment, take a look at the insulation (on electrical cords, for example) to be sure there are no exposed electrical wires.

Electrical Protective Devices

Electrical protective devices, including fuses, circuit breakers, and ground-fault circuit-interrupters (GFCIs), are critically important to electrical safety. These devices interrupt current flow when it exceeds the capacity of the conductor and should be installed where necessary.

Current can exceed the capacity of the conductor when a motor is overloaded, for example, when you ask a 10 horsepower motor to do the work of a 12 horsepower motor, or when a fault occurs, as when insulation fails in a circuit.

When a circuit is overloaded, the insulation becomes brittle over time. Eventually, it may crack and the circuit fails, or faults.

Fault occurs in two ways. Most of the time a fault will occur between a conductor and an enclosure. This is called a ground fault. Infrequently, a fault will occur between two conductors. This is called a short circuit.

A device which prevents current from exceeding the conductor's capacity creates a weak link in the circuit. In the case of a fuse, the fuse is destroyed before another part of the system is destroyed. In the case of a circuit breaker, a set of contacts opens the circuit. Unlike a fuse, a circuit breaker can be reused by reclosing the contacts. Fuses and circuit breakers are designed to protect equipment and facilities, and in so doing, they also provide considerable protection against shock.

However, the only electrical protective device whose sole purpose is to protect people is the ground-fault circuit-interrupter. The GFCI is not an overcurrent device. It senses an imbalance in current flow over the normal path and opens the circuit. GFCIs are usually installed on circuits that are operated near water.

Guarding

Any live parts of electrical equipment operating at 50 volts or more must be guarded to avoid accidental contact. This protection can be accomplished in several different ways. The machinery or equipment can be located:

- In a room, enclosure, or vault accessible only to qualified personnel.

- Behind substantial covers, panels, or partitions which prevent easy access.

- On a balcony, platform, or gallery area which is elevated and not accessible to unqualified/unauthorized persons.

- At least eight feet above the floor of the work area.

Any entrance to an area containing exposed live parts of electrical equipment must be marked with conspicuous warning signs. These signs should forbid entrance except by qualified persons.

Grounding

Grounding is necessary to protect you from electrical shock, safeguard against fire, and protect against damage to electrical equipment. There are two kinds of grounding:

- Electrical circuit or system grounding, accomplished when one conductor of the circuit is intentionally connected to earth, protects the circuit should lightning strike or other high voltage contact occur. Grounding a system also stabilizes the voltage in the system so expected voltage levels are not exceeded under normal conditions.

• Electrical equipment grounding occurs when the equipment grounding conductor provides a path for dangerous fault current to return to the system ground at the supply source of the circuit should the insulation fail.

When a tool or other piece of electrical equipment is grounded, a low-resistance path is intentionally created to the earth. This path has enough current-carrying capacity to prevent any buildup of voltages in the equipment which could pose a hazard to an employee using the equipment. Therefore, never remove the ground prong from a plug because the equipment no longer protects you from short circuits. If you're touching an ungrounded tool, you will become the path of least resistance to the ground.

Grounding does not guarantee that an employee will never receive a shock or be injured or killed by electricity in the workplace. However, this simple procedure will substantially reduce the likelihood of such accidents. Be sure any equipment you work on is properly grounded.

Safe Work Practices for Handling Electricity

If your job requires you to work on or near exposed energized parts, you should be sure that any tools you use are in good repair, that you use good judgment when working near electrical lines, and that you use appropriate protective equipment.

Personal Protective Equipment

If you work on or near exposed energized parts, you must be trained as a qualified person. Your employer must provide you with protective equipment. You must use electrical protective equipment (see 29 CFR 1910.137) appropriate for the body parts that need protection and for the work to be done. Electrical protective equipment includes insulating blankets, matting, gloves, sleeves, overshoes, face protection, and hard hats among other equipment specially made to protect you from electricity.

Lockout/Tagout

Before any repair work or inspection of a piece of electrical equipment is begun by a qualified person, the current must be turned off at the switch box, and the switch padlocked in the OFF position.

The other step in this procedure is the tagging of the switch or controls of the machine or other equipment which is currently locked out of service. The tag indicates which circuits or pieces of equipment are out of service.

Work at Working Safely

Safety should be foremost in your mind when working with electrical equipment. You face hazards from the tools themselves and the electricity that powers them. It's up to you to wear protective equipment whenever it's specified, use all safety procedures, and work with tools correctly. The following general rules apply to every piece of electrical equipment you use:

• Be sure your electrical equipment is maintained properly. Regularly inspect tools, cords, grounds, and accessories. Make repairs only if you are authorized to do so. Otherwise, arrange to have equipment repaired or replaced immediately.

- Be sure you use safety features like three-prong plugs, double-insulated tools, and safety switches. Be sure electrical covers and panels are in place and that you always follow proper procedures.

- Install or repair equipment only if you're qualified and authorized to do so. A faulty job may cause a fire or seriously injure you or other workers.

- Keep electric cables and cords clean and free from kinks. Never carry equipment by its cords.

- Use extension cords only when flexibility is necessary:

  o **Never** use them as substitutes for fixed wiring.

  o **Never** run them through holes in walls, ceilings, floors, doorways, or windows.

  o **Never** use them where they are concealed behind walls, ceilings, or floors.

- Don't touch water, damp surfaces, ungrounded metal, or any bare wires if you are not protected. Qualified employees must wear approved rubber gloves when working with live wires or ungrounded surfaces, and wear electrically-insulated shoes or boots.

- Don't wear metal objects (rings, watches, etc.) when working with electricity. They might cause arcing.

- If you are working near overhead power lines of 50 kilovolts (kV) or less, you or any equipment you are using must not come any closer than 10 ft from the lines. Add 4 inches of distance for every 10 kV over 50 kV.

Good work habits soon become second nature. Treat electricity with the respect it deserves, and it will serve you efficiently and safely.

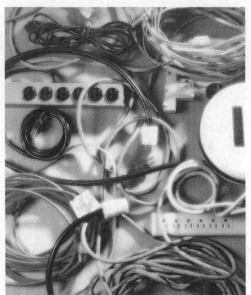

Safe at Home

Electrical hazards at home are just as deadly as they are in the workplace. To keep yourself and your family safe from electrical fires, shocks, and electrocutions:

- Regularly inspect electrical appliances for damage such as exposed wiring, cut or cracked insulation, or cracked or missing guards over electrical parts.

- Don't overload outlets by plugging in too many appliances.

- Don't use electrical appliances if you notice any heat build-up, sparks, or smoke.

- Have a qualified electrician evaluate your electrical service if you regularly have blown fuses or tripped circuit breakers.

- Be sure outdoor outlets and outlets in the kitchen and bathrooms have GFCI protection.

- Hire a qualified electrician to do home wiring projects.

Employee _____

Instructor _____

Date _____

Location _____

ELECTRICAL SAFETY REVIEW

1. Workers who may work on or near exposed live (energized) parts:
    a. Are "unqualified" workers.
    b. Are "qualified" workers.
    c. Don't need training.
    d. Don't need to know proper clearance distances.

2. If you aren't trained to work on or near exposed live (energized) parts:
    a. You are an "unqualified" worker.
    b. You are a "qualified" worker.
    c. You may not use any electrically powered equipment.
    d. You don't need to know the specific safety practices for your job.

3. The flow of electrons through a conductor:
    a. Causes static.
    b. Is the generating source.
    c. Makes up an electrical current.
    d. Describes how a switch operates.

4. A complete circuit is made up of:
    a. A load (device that consumes electricity).
    b. A conductor.
    c. A source of electricity.
    d. All of the above.

5. You will get an electrical shock if:
    a. You are wearing gloves.
    b. You are an "unqualified" worker.
    c. A part of your body completes an electrical circuit.
    d. A GFCI is installed.

6. When electromotive force is exerted:
   a. Electrons flow through a conductor.
   b. An arc-blast occurs.
   c. There is a fire.
   d. Workers must wear gloves.

7. The term "amperes" is used to describe:
   a. The brightness of a light bulb.
   b. The number of ohms.
   c. The amount of current in a circuit.
   d. The poles of a battery.

8. If a person has small burn marks on his skin after receiving an electric shock:
   a. These surface burns are his only injury.
   b. He can have internal injuries, such as nerve or muscle damage.
   c. He was not really shocked.
   d. The current was not large enough to cause any injury.

9. Fires can result from:
   a. Using defective or damaged electrical equipment.
   b. High resistance connections.
   c. Improperly spliced or connected wires.
   d. All of the above.

10. Circuit breakers and ground-fault circuit-interrupters (GFCIs) are examples of:
    a. Insulation.
    b. Guarding.
    c. Electrical protective devices.
    d. Personal protective equipment.

EMERGENCY RESPONSE

In a world that increasingly relies on chemicals, the transportation, handling, and storage of those substances concern everyone. Hazardous chemical spills and exposure affect individuals, families, communities, and the ecological health of the entire planet.

Good planning is essential to safe chemical handling. That is why any organization that deals with hazardous chemicals will have:

* An emergency response team in place, or

* Made arrangements with an outside contractor to respond to chemical emergencies.

Although you do your best to avoid accidents, mishaps with toxic chemicals still occur. When a hazardous chemical spills in your plant, you need to know the correct steps to take.

Where Are the Regulations?

The Occupational Safety and Health Administration (OSHA) has issued the Hazardous Waste Operations and Emergency Response (HAZWOPER) standard. It is found at 29 CFR 1910.120.

Some employers covered by HAZWOPER decide to evacuate all employees in the event of a chemical emergency. These employers do not allow workers to assist in handling the spill and must have an emergency action plan (EAP) in place. Regulations covering EAPs are found at 29 CFR 1910.38.

Emergency Action Plans

You should be familiar with:

- How to report fires, hazardous chemical spills, and other emergencies.

- The route you are assigned to take during a building evacuation.

- Who to ask for more information.

Alarm Systems

Most employers use alarm systems to tell employees that they should evacuate an area or take a specific action. You must be able to recognize these alarms. In areas where production noise could prevent an alarm from being heard, flashing lights are often installed as a second, visual alarm. These alarm systems often have auxiliary power sources so that they can operate even when the power goes out.

Emergency Shutdown of Equipment

If time permits before evacuation, turn off any equipment you are operating, such as forklifts or conveyors. Your employer may designate certain workers to shut down critical facility systems, such as gas and electrical power, before evacuating the work area.

Evacuation

Your employer will develop emergency evacuation routes for the various locations in your facility. Floor plans or work-area maps that clearly define emergency escape routes are commonly used to convey this information.

Emergency evacuation procedures may also indicate shelter areas, such as locker rooms and cafeterias that are structurally sound, to be used as shelter during a tornado, for example.

Your employer will designate certain employees to take a head count of all workers after evacuation and to inform emergency responders of any missing personnel.

Emergency Response Plans

Those employers who choose to handle chemical spills themselves must follow stringent requirements. Very specific training is necessary when preparing to handle emergency chemical releases. Training levels range from awareness training for first response to technical training for those with responsibility for solving problems associated with spill cleanup. **Under no circumstances does OSHA permit personnel without appropriate training to respond to a chemical spill emergency**.

The following information in this chapter outlines some considerations in handling a chemical spill emergency and **assumes that appropriate training has occurred**.

Your Role in the Event of a Spill

Whether it's a solid or a liquid spill, remember that you can be exposed to toxic dust or vapor without even knowing it. If you are properly trained, respond to a hazardous chemical spill with care and speed. However, if you have *not received training*, get to a safe place and sound an alarm according to established policy. At the least, a supervisor should be notified. Cooperate with the emergency response team.

KNOW Potential Hazards.

The safety data sheet (SDS) is one of your best sources of information on the chemicals used in your area. The emergency response team needs to have SDSs at hand before responding to a spill.

KNOW About Spill Equipment.

The response team knows where the emergency equipment is and how to use it.

KNOW the Location of Fire Extinguishers.

Many chemicals are flammable or create a flammable product when mixed. In most cases of fire, you should get yourself and others out of the work area quickly and call for help. Trained employees use an appropriate fire extinguisher only if the fire is contained and is not rapidly spreading.

KNOW the Location of Emergency Exits.

Make sure you know how to get out of your work area or the building quickly if necessary. Keep aisles clear so that you and co-workers are not endangered because of a slow exit from the scene of a toxic spill.

KNOW First Aid or Where to Get It.

Know the general first aid rules and what the SDSs say about first aid for the particular substances you work with.

The Emergency Response Team

Members of an emergency response team go through training on:

- Personnel roles.

- Communications.

- Lines of authority.

- Emergency recognition and prevention.

- Places of refuge.

- Site security.

- Evacuation routes.

- Emergency medical care.

The object is for the team to perform its job with minimal risks. Team members must know the limits for themselves and their equipment. They need to know how to safely avoid or escape emergency situations. Members of the response team use the buddy system — they never enter a chemical emergency situation alone.

Evacuation During Spill Response

Response team leaders will consider evacuation as soon as a spill is evaluated. The decision to evacuate will depend on the chemical and the hazards involved.

Evacuation can be as simple as clearing people from the immediate area of the spill or as complicated as total evacuation of the plant, surrounding area, and community. In total evacuations involving the community, proper public safety personnel must be involved.

PPE for Chemical Handling

The hazardous chemicals used at your plant or work site determine the level of personal protective equipment (PPE) and clothing. Emergency response team members receive necessary instruction and training on PPE and clothing.

The Environmental Protection Agency has set four levels of personal protection, A through D, with A providing the most protection:

- Level A PPE consists of the most protective type of respirator; a fully encapsulating, chemical-type resistant suit; inner and outer rubber gloves; rubber boots and steel toe safety boots; and a two-way radio. A hard hat may also be needed.

- Level B consists of the same type of respiratory protection as Level A; disposable, hooded chemical-resistant coveralls; rubber boots and steel toe safety boots; inner and outer rubber gloves; and a two-way radio. A hard hat may also be needed.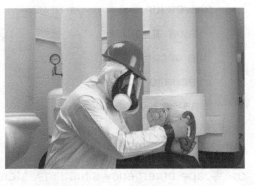

- Level C includes the same personal protective clothing mentioned for Level B, but with an air-purifying respirator.

- Level D consists of a basic work uniform that provides minimal chemical protection. Level D may be used where contamination is at nuisance levels only. Level D may include coveralls, eye protection, safety shoes, gloves, etc.

Spill Carts and Spill Control Stations

To deal with spills and other accidents, spill carts and spill control stations are frequently used. Response team members know the location of the carts and stations. Keep them accessible and well stocked. Again, you will receive instruction and training as your job requires.

Typical items found in spill carts (or wagons) and spill control stations are:

- Pillows, pads, or other materials designed to collect, neutralize, absorb, or suppress hazardous liquids while picking up a spill.

- Patch and plug kits.

- Brooms, shovels, mops, scrapers, squeegees, and buckets.

- Both acid and base neutralizers.

- Temporary warning labels.

- Tapes and barricades.

- Coveralls, goggles, and gloves.

- Salvage drums and waste containers.

The response team must make sure they have the supplies and equipment they need for the work area — and that they have adequate quantities.

Decontamination Procedures

A decontamination plan needs to be part of every plant's emergency response effort. Equipment and PPE must be decontaminated after use. Planning ahead makes sense. Dispose of chemically contaminated waste properly.

Emergency Follow-up Is Essential

Following an emergency, OSHA must be notified if the incident resulted in any fatalities or hospitalizations. If the spill is significant, the National Response Center must be notified as well. The Environmental Protection Agency regulates chemical releases to the environment.

The final activity of the emergency response team is to review and evaluate all aspects of what happened and what may happen as a result. An account of the incident must be accurate, authentic, and complete, so be prepared to cooperate.

Work at Working Safely

Remember, the best accident and spill control is accident and spill prevention. But in the event of a spill:

1. Tell others a spill has occurred and help them get to safety.

2. Report the spill to management.

3. Don't ignore a spill. It can produce harmful or deadly vapors.

4. Don't endanger your own life. If fire or explosion seem imminent, get out of the work area.

Safe at Home

You probably don't have chemicals around the house that would trigger an emergency response for a spill or release. But, you and your family should know what to do if there's a gas leak in your home. Natural gas and propane supplies are treated with a chemical agent that gives the gas a rotten egg odor. Instruct your family to immediately evacuate the building and call the fire department if they smell a gas leak.

Have any new or replacement gas-fired appliances professionally installed. Have a gas-fired furnace or boiler professionally cleaned and inspected every year. Contact your gas utility supplier for more information on the safe use of gas in the home.

If you need to check gas lines, hoses, or fittings for leaks (for example, when checking the connection of a portable tank to an outdoor grill), always use a soapy water solution and watch for bubbles. Never use a match or other open flame to check gas lines, hoses, or fittings for leaks.

Employee _____

Instructor _____

Date _____

Location _____

EMERGENCY RESPONSE REVIEW

1. When a release of hazardous chemicals on-site would need an emergency response, an organization has:
   a. An emergency response team in place.
   b. Arranged with an outside contractor to respond to chemical emergencies.
   c. Either a. or b.
   d. Neither a. nor b.

2. When the employer has an emergency action plan in place:
   a. Workers aren't allowed to assist in handling the response to a chemical spill.
   b. Workers are required to assist in handling the response to a chemical spill.
   c. Some employees evacuate if there is a chemical emergency.
   d. No employees evacuate if there is a chemical emergency.

3. Under an emergency action plan, employees should be familiar with:
   a. The requirement to finish their work before they evacuate in an emergency.
   b. How to clean up hazardous chemical spills.
   c. How to test the alarm system.
   d. How to report emergencies.

4. What has a back-up power supply so it can operate when the power goes out?
   a. The building's gas supply.
   b. The alarm system.
   c. The building's heating system.
   d. The building's water supply.

5. What isn't part of an emergency evacuation plan?
   a. A head count.
   b. Designated shelter areas.
   c. Escape routes.
   d. A hot work permit.

6. If you discover a chemical emergency, but you have no training to respond to it:
   a. Go to a safe place and sound an alarm.
   b. Stop the release as best you can.
   c. Put on a respirator and PPE as you continue working.
   d. None of the above.

7. What must the emergency response team have at hand before responding to a spill?
   a. A fire extinguisher.
   b. Walkie-talkies.
   c. Safety data sheets.
   d. Permission from the fire department.

8. The members of the emergency response team must:
   a. Take actions to put their lives at risk.
   b. Take actions beyond the safe limits of the equipment they use.
   c. Know how to avoid or escape emergency situations.
   d. Work alone.

9. Acid and base neutralizers are:
   a. Used in most chemical processes.
   b. Extremely hazardous materials.
   c. Stored in salvage drums.
   d. Typical items found on spill carts or at spill control stations.

10. Following an emergency:
    a. OSHA must be notified if there were any fatalities.
    b. The National Response Center may need to be notified.
    c. The emergency response team evaluates what happened.
    d. All of the above.

EYE PROTECTION

When it comes to eye protection, you and your employer share responsibility for your safety. YOU have to take safety seriously and use eye protection as required.

Where Are the Regulations?

Regulations have been issued by the Occupational Safety and Health Administration (OSHA) on personal protective equipment (PPE) in general, and on eye protection in particular. You can find these regulations at 29 CFR 1910.132-.133.

Your employer must assess the hazards in the workplace to determine if eye and face protection is needed.

You must receive training in the proper use of eye and face protection and understand:

- When eye and face protection is necessary.

- What eye and face protection is necessary.

- How to properly put on, take off, adjust, and wear goggles, face shields, etc.

- PPE limitations.

- Proper care, maintenance, useful life, and disposal of eye and face protection.

You must show that you understand the training and can use eye and face protection properly before you will be allowed to perform work requiring its use.

Eye Injuries Are Often Permanent

An eye injury resulting in blindness cannot be cured. Excuses like "I don't wear my goggles because my hair gets messed up" or "I look silly in safety glasses" seem unimportant when compared with the value of a pair of healthy eyes. Proper eye protection reduces your chances of injury and reduces the severity of injury if an accident does occur.

What Are the Hazards?

Here are some of the causes of eye injuries:

- Injurious gases, vapors, and liquids.

- Flying objects or particles.

- Dusts or powders, fumes and mists.

- Splashing metal.

- Thermal and radiation hazards such as heat, glare, ultraviolet, and infrared rays.

- Lasers.

- Electrical arcing and sparks.

How Can You Protect Your Eyes?

Your employer must identify hazards in your work area to determine how best to avoid eye injuries. Eye hazards can be reduced by using machine guards and shields. PPE is needed if the hazards aren't eliminated. Your employer must also provide eyewash facilities if you are exposed to corrosive materials.

Equipment Guards

Be sure to use any guards, screens, and shields that are attached to equipment. If the guards don't completely eliminate the eye and face hazards, wear eye and face protection.

Movable screens can be used to separate workers at one machine from those at nearby work stations. Portable welding screens can be positioned around welding areas to protect other workers from sparks and radiation.

Eyewash Facilities Are Important

If a chemical splashes in your eyes, move quickly to an emergency shower or eyewash. Look directly into the stream of water and hold your eyes open with your fingers. Flush your eyes for at least 15 minutes and then get medical attention.

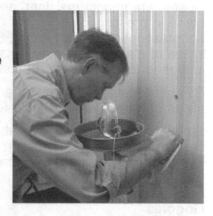

Personal Protective Equipment

A wide variety of safety equipment is available. Protective eye and face equipment must comply with ANSI guidelines and be marked directly on the piece of equipment (e.g. glasses frames and lenses).

Safety Glasses

The most common type of protective equipment for the eyes is safety glasses. They provide protection from flying chips or particles, and they can have tinted lenses for radiation and laser hazards.

They may look like normal street-wear glasses; they are made of glass, plastic, or polycarbonate. But, they are made much stronger than street-wear lenses, are impact resistant, and come in prescription or nonprescription (plano) forms. Some styles of plano safety glasses are designed to fit over prescription glasses.

Safety frames are stronger than street-wear frames. Different styles of frames are available for different jobs.

Safety glasses also are available with side shield guards. Side shields provide protection for the sides of your eyes. Eye-cup side shields provide more thorough eye protection from hazards that come from the front, side, top, or bottom.

Goggles

Goggles are very similar to safety glasses but fit closer to the eyes. They can provide additional protection in hazardous situations involving liquid splashes, fumes, vapors, and dust. Some models can be worn over prescription glasses.

Face Shields

Full-face protection is often required
to guard against molten metal and
chemical splashes. Face shields are
available to fit with a hard hat or to
wear directly on the head. When
you need to wear a face shield,
always wear other eye protection
such as goggles or safety glasses
under it.

Cleaning

You should maintain and clean your
eye protection regularly. Use lens
cleaners recommended by the
equipment's manufacturer or mild soap and warm water.
Strong solvents can damage the lenses. Dirty, scratched, or
cracked lenses reduce vision and seriously reduce protection.
Replace damaged eye and face protection immediately.

What About Contact Lenses?

Most workers can safely wear their contacts on the job.

It is important to remember that your contacts should be worn
along with additional eye protection.

It's also a good idea to keep a spare pair of contacts or
prescription glasses with you in case the pair you usually
wear is lost or damaged while you're working. You might also
want to make sure your supervisor or plant first aid personnel
know that you wear contacts, in the event of any injury on the
job.

When Are Absorptive Lenses Required?

Absorptive lenses are used to absorb or screen out unwanted
light and glare. Most ordinary sunglasses do not provide the
right glare protection. For welding or work with torches,
goggles or helmets are available with filter lenses to shield
the eyes from radiation and glare.

Work at Working Safely

Let's review the following important rules about eye safety:

1. Match safety equipment to the degree of hazard present.
2. Know what protective devices are available on the job and how they can protect you.
3. Make sure machine guards are in place.
4. Know the location and operation of emergency eyewash equipment.
5. Street-wear eyeglasses are not designed to be safety glasses and should never be used as such.
6. Faceshields should not be used alone, but always with other eye protection such as goggles or glasses.
7. Make sure any safety device you use fits properly.
8. Safety equipment should be maintained in good condition and replaced when defective.

Safe at Home

Flying objects, chips, and particles; dust; mist; and chemical splashes can injure your eyes during home projects as easily as they can hurt you at work.

A good practice when selecting eye protection for use at home is to:

- Wear safety glasses with side shields or wear goggles to protect your eyes from objects, particles, or chips that could fly off during tool use or fall into your eyes while reaching overhead to work.

- Wear safety goggles to protect your eyes from splashes of liquids, mists, or dusts.

Get prompt medical attention if you suffer an eye injury at home.

Employee _____

Instructor _____

Date _____

Location _____

EYE PROTECTION REVIEW

1. You must know how to properly put on, adjust, and wear eye and face protection:
   a. Only if you are new on the job.
   b. Only after you have had an eye injury.
   c. If you need to use eye and face protection on the job.
   d. Only if you are the person assigned to clean eye and face protection.

2. Before you will be allowed to do work that requires the use of eye protection:
   a. You must receive training.
   b. You must show that you understand the training.
   c. You must show that you can use the eye protection properly.
   d. All of the above.

3. Wearing proper eye and face protection:
   a. Will only protect you from serious injuries that can cause blindness.
   b. Will not reduce the severity of an injury if an accident occurs.
   c. Is only required if you feel like wearing it.
   d. Reduces you chance of being injured.

4. Which of the following isn't a common cause of work-related eye injuries?
   a. Flying objects or particles.
   b. Dusts and powders.
   c. Heat, glare, and infrared rays.
   d. Wearing sunglasses at night.

5. Who must identify workplace hazards to determine how to best avoid eye injuries?
   a. Machine operators.
   b. The employer.
   c. OSHA.
   d. The insurance company.

6. If machine guards and shields eliminate eye hazards:
   a. You must wear a face shield in addition to goggles.
   b. You must wear a face shield even if you don't need eye protection.
   c. You would not need to wear eye and face protection.
   d. You would not need training, but you would need to wear eye protection.

7. Moveable, portable screens are often used:
   a. If employees don't have safety glasses.
   b. To separate workers from hazards created by a nearby work station.
   c. To protect other workers from welding sparks and radiation.
   d. Both b. and c.

8. Eyewash facilities:
   a. Must be provided if workers are exposed to corrosive materials.
   b. Eliminate the need for getting medical attention.
   c. Need to be used for only about five minutes to treat an injury.
   d. Work better if you keep your eyes closed tightly.

9. Normal, street-wear prescription glasses:
   a. Offer the same protection as safety glasses.
   b. Have frames and lenses that aren't as strong as safety glasses.
   c. May not be worn under non-prescription safety glasses or goggles.
   d. Always have side shield guards.

10. What can provide tight-fitting protection from splashes, vapors, and dust?
    a. Safety glasses.
    b. Goggles.
    c. Face shields.
    d. Welding helmets.

FALL PROTECTION

Falls from elevations are the leading cause of death in general industry workplaces. They can happen in all occupations and in a variety of work settings — from the employee washing windows 40 feet from the ground to the stock clerk retrieving goods from a shelf using a ladder. Thankfully, these types of falls can be prevented by using proper fall protection.

Fall protection is any equipment, device, or system that prevents a worker from falling from an elevation or mitigates the effect of such a fall.

Your employer must provide you with fall protection if you are assigned a job that exposes you to a fall hazard four feet or more above a lower level. Fall protection must also be provided regardless of height in certain situations, such as working above dangerous equipment. The types of fall protection you may use include:

- Covers,
- Designated areas,
- Guardrails,
- Handrails,
- Personal fall protection,
- Ladder safety system, and
- Safety nets.

If you use one of these fall protection systems, you must be trained.

Where Are the Regulations?

The Occupational Safety and Health Administration (OSHA) has rules governing fall protection. These rules are found at 29 CFR 1910.29, .30, and .140. This requires your employer to:

- Provide you with fall protection if you are exposed to fall hazards;

- Train you on how to recognize and minimize these fall hazards;

- Train you on how to inspect, install, use, disassemble, and maintain the fall protection; and

- Retrain you when you demonstrate a lack of understanding or skill about the fall protection you use.

Covers

Covers are secured, removable caps used to protect you from falling into holes in floors, roofs, skylights, manholes, pits, and other walking-working surfaces.

Any cover used must be capable of supporting at least twice the maximum intended load that will be placed on it. In other words, if you walk across a cover, it must be able to support you, as well as any equipment, tools, materials, and vehicles you may be carrying or using.

Also, covers must be firmly secured at all times to prevent movement. This can be caused by a number of factors, including wind, flooding, ice, and snow. Heavy equipment running back and forth over covers also can loosen or displace them.

Designated Areas

A designated area is a type of fall protection that can only be used on a low-slope roof. A low-slope roof is often called a "flat roof." If you work on a low-slope roof, you may use a designated area to protect you from falls off the edge.

Fall protection is provided via a warning line. The line is a barrier that marks or delineates only the area in which you are allowed to work without additional fall protection, and warns you about the fall hazard at the roof edge. It can be constructed out of rope, wire, tape, or chain, but must be:

- Capable of withstanding 200 pounds of pressure before the line breaks,

- A height of 34 to 39 inches at its lowest point, and

- Clearly visible from 25 feet away.

These requirements help make sure that you are safe from falls at all times when working in a designated area. If you use a designated area, you must be trained. This includes understanding proper:

- Setup,

- Use, and

- Disassembly.

Guardrails

Guardrails — also called railings — have been the primary means of preventing employees from falling to lower levels in workplaces for decades.

A guardrail is a physical barrier. It consists of a top rail, midrail, and posts. Guardrails are used to protect you from falls from the unprotected or exposed sides and edges of walking-working surfaces, like a platform or mezzanine.

Guardrails must be constructed of certain materials to:

- Provide adequate strength should you fall into the guardrail,

- Protect you from injury (e.g., puncture and lacerations), and

- Prevent catching or snagging your clothing.

Guardrails are also required to have:

- A top rail that is between 39 and 45 inches high,

- A midrail that is halfway between the top rail and the walking-working surface below, and

- Vertical posts that are no more than 19 inches apart.

All of these guardrail requirements are intended to provide adequate fall protection.

Handrails

Handrails are also a type of fall protection. A handrail is a rail used to provide you with a handhold for support. They must be used as fall protection on flights of stairs having at least three treads and at least four risers. These requirements are dependent upon stairway width and the number of enclosed sides.

Personal Fall Protection

Another type of fall protection is personal fall protection. This is protection that is worn on your body. This may be familiar to you already, but OSHA says this includes three types:

1. Personal fall arrest,

2. Travel restraint, and

3. Positioning devices.

Personal Fall Arrest

Personal fall arrest is a system that arrests you in a fall. This means that the system stops you before hitting the floor, ground, etc. This fall protection consists of a:

*   Body harness,

*   Anchorage, and

*   Connector.

The body harness is made of straps that are worn in a manner that distributes fall arrest forces over your thighs, pelvis, waist, chest, and shoulders should a fall occur. It's critical that the harness is worn correctly and securely to prevent you from falling out of it during a fall. It also helps support your body in midair after a fall.

The anchorage is a point of attachment for the personal fall arrest system. The strength of any fall protection system is based on it being connected to a secure anchorage point. When falling six feet, a person will exert up to 10 times their body weight on the system. This is why an anchorage point must be capable of supporting at least 5,000 pounds for each employee that is attached to it or be designed as part of a complete personal fall protection system.

A connector is a device used to connect together parts of the personal fall arrest system. Examples of connectors include snaphooks, carabiners, buckles, and D-rings. A connector can also be a lanyard, deceleration device, or lifeline that connects the body harness to the anchorage point.

Travel Restraint

Travel restraint is a system that eliminates the possibility of a fall. It limits your movement so that you can't get close to an unprotected side or edge of a walking-working surface. Like personal fall arrest, this system can consist of several components, including:

* Body harness or body belt,

* Anchorage, and

* Lanyard.

A lanyard is a flexible line of rope, wire rope, or strap which generally has a connector at each end. This is to connect the body belt or body harness to a deceleration device, lifeline, or anchorage point.

Positioning Device

A positioning device allows you to be supported on an elevated vertical surface, like a wall or window sill, so that work can be done with both of your hands. You are always in a fixed position and cannot move freely as you can if wearing a personal fall arrest or travel restraint system. The system consists of equipment and connectors used with a body harness or body belt.

If you use personal fall protection, you must be trained to understand correct:

* Hook-up,

- Anchoring, and

- Tie-off techniques.

Also, personal fall protection must only be used for fall protection and not for any other purpose, such as hoisting equipment or materials. This could weaken fibers, cause tears or frays, stretch metal, etc. This type of damage would make the fall protection unsafe to use.

This is why all types of personal fall protection must be inspected before initial use during each workshift for:

- Mildew,

- Wear,

- Damage, and

- Deterioration (e.g., rust).

This inspection helps makes certain that the system is safe, so any component which is found to be defective cannot be used.

Ladder Safety System

A ladder safety system is another type of fall protection. It is designed to prevent you from hitting a lower level by eliminating or reducing the possibility of falling from a fixed ladder. It usually consists of a carrier (i.e., lifeline), safety sleeve, lanyard, connectors, and body harness.

The carrier is a rigid or flexible track attached to or immediately adjacent to fixed ladders. The safety sleeve is a moving component that travels on the carrier. A ladder safety system must be designed so that it doesn't require you to continuously hold, push, or pull any part of the system.

This allows you to move up and down the fixed ladder with both hands free for climbing. This also allows you to perform a task when you stop climbing.

If you use a ladder safety system, you must be trained on how to properly:

• Inspect the system before use,

• Use the system, and

• Maintain the system.

Safety Nets

Another fall protection system available to employers are safety nets. Safety nets are used to protect you from hazardous vertical drops. They can be used to protect you on several types of elevated walking-working surfaces, including:

• Unprotected sides and edges,

• Wall openings, and

• Low-slope roofs.

This device is a horizontal or semi-horizontal barrier that uses a netting system to catch and stop falling workers, as well as tools and equipment, before they make contact with the surface or structures below. To be effective, they must be installed as close as possible under where you are working, but never more than 30 feet below the edge of a walking-working surface. Safety nets should also extend outward from the edge of your work.

Materials, scrap pieces, equipment, and tools which have fallen into the safety net must be removed as soon as possible and at least before the next work shift.

Safety nets must be inspected at least once a week for:

• Wear,

• Damage, and

• Deterioration.

Safety nets must also be inspected after any occurrence which could affect the integrity of the system. Defective nets cannot be used.

Work at Working Safety

Falls are a leading cause of death in general industry workplaces. Take these precautions as you work:

- Understand the fall hazards to which you may be exposed in your work area;

- Use proper fall protection to minimize these fall hazards;

- Correctly install, set-up, inspect, operate/use, maintain, disassemble, and/or store fall protection systems; and

- Report fall hazards.

FALL PROTECTION

Employee _____

Instructor _____

Date _____

Location _____

FALL PROTECTION REVIEW

1. You must be provided with fall protection if you are:
   a. Exposed to fall hazards.
   b. Seeing fall hazards.
   c. Thinking about fall hazards.
   d. Talking about fall hazards.

2. The purpose of fall protection is to:
   a. Elevate tools above the ground.
   b. Eliminate dangerous equipment.
   c. Prevent you from falling.
   d. All of the above.

3. You must be provided with fall protection at:
   a. Two feet and above.
   b. Four feet and above.
   c. Exactly six feet.
   d. Below ten feet.

4. Covers are used to prevent you from falling into:
   a. Stairs.
   b. Holes.
   c. Tools.
   d. Aisles.

5. Designated areas can only be used on top of:
   a. Low-slope roofs.
   b. Equipment.
   c. Trailers.
   d. Platforms.

71

6. A guardrail is a physical barrier that consists of:
   a. A top rail.
   b. A midrail.
   c. Posts.
   d. All of the above.

7. Types of personal fall protection include:
   a. Personal fall arrest.
   b. Travel restraint.
   c. Positioning devices.
   d. All of the above.

8. Personal fall protection must be inspected before use for:
   a. Mildew.
   b. Wear.
   c. Damage.
   d. All of the above.

9. A ladder safety system prevents falls from:
   a. Portable ladders.
   b. Mobile ladder stands.
   c. Fixed ladders.
   d. Stepstools.

10. If provided fall protection, you must be trained on how to:
    a. Inspect it.
    b. Use it.
    c. Maintain it.
    d. All of the above.

FIRE PREVENTION

The best defense against a fire is to prevent a fire from starting in the first place. Although many products stored in a warehouse or work area are not flammable, some packaging types commonly used today, such as cardboard, foam compositions, and paper packing are definite fire hazards. In addition, some of the chemicals you work with may be able to start or feed a fire. And, faulty wiring can start an electrical fire in any workplace.

You need to know what to do to keep fires from starting, as well as how to deal with a fire emergency.

Where Are the Regulations?

The Occupational Safety and Health Administration (OSHA) regulates several aspects of fire prevention and response. Fire prevention plans are addressed in 29 CFR 1910.39. In addition, the provisions for fire extinguishers and other protection are addressed at 29 CFR 1910.157.

What Kind of Fire Is It?

The National Fire Protection Association (NFPA) has classified five general types of fires, based on the combustible materials involved and the kind of extinguisher needed to put them out. The five fire classifications are A, B, C, D, and K.

General Classes of Fires

Class A. This type of fire is the most common. The combustible materials are wood, cloth, paper, rubber, and plastic. The common extinguishing agent is water, but dry chemicals are also effective.

Class B. Flammable liquids, gases, and greases create class B fires. The most common extinguisher to use is dry chemical. Also, foam and carbon dioxide extinguishers can be used.

Class C. Because class C fires are electrical fires, use a nonconducting agent to put them out, for example, carbon dioxide and dry chemical extinguishers. Never use foam or water-type extinguishers on these fires.

Class D. Fires arising from combustible metals, such as magnesium, titanium, zirconium, and sodium are categorized as class D fires. These fires require specialized techniques to extinguish them. None of the common extinguishers should be used. Use dry powder extinguishers specific for the metal hazard present on these fires.

Class K. Fires resulting from the combustion of cooking oils and fats are class K fires. Commercial kitchens usually have special extinguishers for class K fires.

Multi-purpose extinguishers (ABC) will handle all A, B, and C fires. **Be sure to read the label.**

Housekeeping to Prevent Fires

The importance of good housekeeping ties in closely with fire prevention. If you allow debris or flammable material to accumulate, the risk of starting a fire increases. Everyone must help to keep the work area clutter-free and safe from other fire hazards, such as improperly used or stored chemicals.

Fire Checklist

When a fire starts, think first of your safety and the safety of others. Alert the fire department. Try to put out the fire only if you have been trained to use extinguishers and the fire is small and tame enough to be extinguished by a hand-held extinguisher.

When the fire is spreading quickly, the combustible material is unknown, or you have not been trained in the proper use of extinguishers, leave the fire fighting to professionals with the proper equipment. In this case, sound the fire alarm, and evacuate.

If the fire can be contained or extinguished, **a properly trained person should use the right extinguisher on the fire**. When using a typical extinguisher, follow the "PASS" method. Hold the extinguisher upright, and:

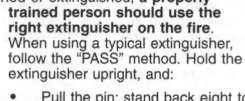

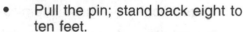

- Pull the pin; stand back eight to ten feet.

- Aim at the base of the fire.

- Squeeze the handle.

- Sweep at the base of the fire with the extinguishing agent.

Remember, too, that most extinguishers have a very limited operation time, only 8-10 seconds, so you have to act fast and spray correctly at the base of the fire.

Know the location of fire alarms and extinguishers. Know your nearest fire exit, and proceed to it in an orderly fashion.

Smoke and fumes can leave a person unconscious. All fires consume oxygen to burn. Most victims of a fire suffocate from lack of oxygen and die. They are already unconscious or dead before the flames reach them.

Inside a building that is in flames, get to your hands and knees and crawl to an exit. This is important because smoke and heat rise rapidly, and you will inhale less smoke near the floor. Outside, get upwind of the smoke.

The Chemical Fire

Many of the thousands of chemicals in use in the workplace are both highly toxic and highly volatile. Extreme caution must be used to prevent and fight fires resulting from chemical spills and accidents. Know the hazards of the chemical substances you use on the job and how to handle and store them properly to prevent dangerous chemical fires.

Chemical Hazards

Chemicals can cause serious injuries through physical (fire or explosion) or health (burns or poisons) hazards. Many chemicals have inherent properties that make them very hazardous.

They might include:

- **Flammability** — These chemicals catch fire very easily.

- **Reactivity** — A reactive material can undergo a chemical reaction under certain conditions; reactive substances can burn, explode, or release toxic vapor if exposed to other chemicals, air, or water.

- **Explosivity** — An explosive can undergo a very rapid chemical reaction producing large amounts of gas and heat.

As a result of these properties, chemicals can produce fires that start and spread quickly.

Flammable Liquid Handling and Storage

Flammable liquids give off ignitable vapors. Also, nearly all flammable liquid vapors are heavier than air and will accumulate in low areas with poor ventilation. When they accumulate sufficiently, they spread and can travel to an ignition source. These ignition sources might be cigarettes, a hand tool that sparks, a cutting torch, or a motor.

Storage

The typical plant stores flammable liquids in two ways: reserve storage in drums and operational storage in small quantities (for use at work stations.) For reserve storage safety, as soon as a drum is unloaded, the bung cap should be replaced with a drum vent; this prevents pressure build-up if the drum is exposed to heat. Proper vents also incorporate emergency relief devices, which blow out under extreme pressure.

Drums should also be connected to a grounding system; this eliminates static electrical build-up when dispensing from the drum. If your plant does not have a drum storage room, drums should be stored in a safety cabinet; they are available in sizes to hold drums vertically or horizontally.

Transfer

Liquids can be dispensed from drums by two methods: gravity flow from drums stored horizontally, and pumping from drums stored vertically.

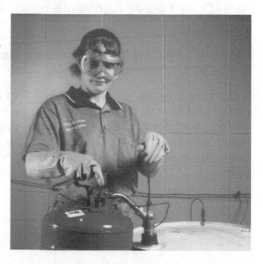

For gravity flow safety, liquids are dispensed into a safety can using a self-closing drum valve. OSHA requires the use of approved safety cans for transfer purposes.

FIRE

A drip can should be placed under the valve to catch spills and leaks. The drip can and receiving container must be bonded to the drum to draw off any static electrical charge.

The pump method is faster, empties the drum almost completely, and saves space because drums are stored vertically. Drip cans are not required. Bond the receiving containers if the pump hoses are not self-bonding.

Mobile solvent tanks (liquid caddies) are used to distribute flammable liquids to work stations using large production line equipment. They are equipped with rubber wheels, a measuring pump, and a self-bonding hose.

Use

Use safety cans to hold and dispense flammable liquids as you work. There are many work station cans from which to choose. Keep containers closed when not in use, and put containers back into safety cabinets for storage.

Disposal

Disposing of waste flammable liquids requires proper procedures. Oily, solvent-soaked rags can easily start a fire. To prevent this, specially designed waste cans should always be used for temporary storage. These cans have spring-loaded lids and a raised bottom with vent holes to dispense heat. Collect waste flammable liquids in approved liquid disposal cans.

Dipping and Coating Operations Using Flammable Liquids

A dip tank means a container holding a liquid other than water and that is used for dipping or coating. Examples of dipping and coating operations are paint dipping, electroplating, pickling, quenching, tanning, degreasing, stripping, cleaning, roll coating, flow coating, and curtain coating.

Dip tanks for flammable and combustible liquids are designed and installed with fire prevention safeguards, but employees need to be aware of some other fire prevention procedures:

- To prevent sparks that can cause fires, electrical wiring and electrical equipment used in the area of the dip tank must be approved for a hazardous location.

- If portable containers are used to pour flammable or combustible liquids into the dip tank, there is a risk that the pouring action could cause sparks due to static electricity discharge. To prevent this, wires must be used to ground and bond portable containers to the dip tank.

- The dip tank area must be kept free of any combustible debris. Rags contaminated with flammable or combustible liquids must be placed in approved waste cans immediately after use. The waste must be properly disposed of at the end of each shift.

- Smoking is prohibited near dip tanks containing flammable or combustible liquids.

- Fire extinguishers must be available in the area.

There are other safe procedures to follow in any dipping or coating operation:

- Dip tanks must be emptied and ventilated before cleaning. Employees who enter a dip tank must follow permit-required confined space entry procedures, as applicable.

- If ventilation does not adequately reduce exposures to hazardous chemicals, employees will need to wear respirators and follow the procedures of the employer's Respiratory Protection Program.

- Employees need to know first aid procedures that are appropriate to the hazards of the operation.

- If the liquids could harm employees' skin, the employer must provide storage space for employees' street clothes, an emergency shower and eye wash station, and basins with hot-water faucets.

Spill Cleanup

Only specially trained emergency response team members may respond to an emergency release or spill.

Specially designed absorbent materials have been developed for spill cleanup. These products are offered in pillows, pads, sheets, tubes, and other shapes to fit all cleanup needs. Once the absorbent material is saturated, it should be placed in a large disposal drum and sealed with a drum cover. Another spill cleanup technique involves the use of specialized vacuum equipment.

Compressed and Liquefied Gases

To avoid fires resulting from ignition of compressed gases:

- Never roll or drag cylinders when gases are stored, transported, or used. Use a hand cart or truck specially designed for gas cylinders.

- Store all cylinders upright and secure them to walls or bench tops during storage or use.

- Compressed gases should be stored in dry, cool and well ventilated areas, protected from the weather, and away from flammable materials. The area should be posted for no smoking.

- Keep compressed gas cylinders which contain oxygen away from oil, grease, or liquid flammables.

- Separate fuel and oxidizing gas cylinders by at least 20 feet or a fire wall.

- Be very careful about fittings or connections. Before any connections are made, inspect the cylinder carefully. Do not change, modify, repair, or tamper with pressure relief devices on cylinders.

- When more information, advice, or help is needed, call the gas supplier; when in doubt about handling, contents, or cylinder condition, seek an expert's advice.

Work at Working Safely

Prevention is the key to eliminating fire hazards:

1. Keep work areas clean and clutter-free.

2. Know how to handle and store the chemicals you work with.

3. Know what you are expected to do in case of a fire emergency.

4. Make sure you are familiar with your facility's emergency action plan for fires.

Safe at Home

It's fairly common for local laws to require homes to have smoke and carbon monoxide detectors installed. This valuable equipment can give you and your family precious time to escape from a fire. Everyone should plan ahead on how the family will evacuate from a fire in the home. Just as you probably have fire drills at work, it's a good idea to practice your home evacuation plan, too. If you hear an alarm, take it seriously and leave the building quickly.

FIRE

To help prevent fires at home:

- Minimize collections of papers, cardboard, and other combustible materials.

- Have a fire extinguisher available, and periodically check to ensure it's properly charged and ready for use.

- Keep your exit routes clear (for example, make sure children put away their toys).

- Supervise children when they help you cook.

- Don't leave candles, fireplaces, or cigarettes unattended, and be sure to extinguish them if you're feeling sleepy.

- If you need to use flammable liquids for a home improvement project, buy only the amount you'll need, and properly dispose of any excess.

Employee _____

Instructor _____

Date _____

Location _____

FIRE PREVENTION REVIEW

1. Some common workplace fire hazards are:
   a. Certain types of chemicals.
   b. Cardboard and paper items could still fuel a fire.
   c. Faulty electrical wiring.
   d. All of the above.

2. Fire classifications are based on:
   a. The location of the fire.
   b. How long the fire has been burning.
   c. The combustible materials involved in the fire.
   d. The amount of training the fire fighter has.

3. Water is a common extinguishing agent for:
   a. Flammable solvents.
   b. Wood, cloth, and paper.
   c. Electrical fires.
   d. Grease fires.

4. The most common extinguishing agent for flammable liquid fires is:
   a. Water fog.
   b. Mist.
   c. Dry chemical.
   d. Sand.

5. Water isn't a good extinguishing agent for electrical fires because:
   a. Water is difficult to use.
   b. Water can't be sprayed at the base of the fire.
   c. Water conducts electricity, so it would add to the hazards.
   d. All of the above.

6. If a combustible metal such as magnesium is on fire:
   a. Use any fire extinguisher to put it out.
   b. No fire extinguisher can put it out.
   c. Use a Class D fire extinguisher.
   d. Use a Class K fire extinguisher.

7. A Class K fire:
   a. Is a common hazard for a commercial kitchen.
   b. Involves cooking oils and fats.
   c. Needs a special type of extinguisher to put it out.
   d. All of the above.

8. Who can help reduce fire hazards by using good housekeeping?
   a. Only maintenance crew members.
   b. Only safety inspectors.
   c. Only fire brigade team members.
   d. Every employee.

9. Who can use a fire extinguisher on a fire?
   a. Only properly trained persons.
   b. Any member of the safety committee.
   c. Only maintenance crew members.
   d. Any supervisor.

10. What eliminates static electrical build-up when pouring or transferring flammable liquids?
   a. Non-sparking tools.
   b. A grounding system.
   c. Drum bung caps.
   d. None of the above.

FIRST AID AND BLOODBORNE PATHOGENS

Like any other job, rendering first aid has its risks. Designated first aid providers need to know how to keep themselves safe while helping an injured person.

What Is First Aid?

First aid is emergency care provided for injury or sudden illness before professional emergency medical care is available. First aid providers are designated by their employer, and they are trained to use a limited amount of equipment to perform an initial 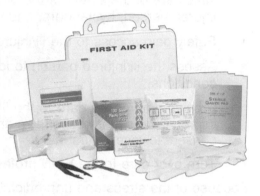 assessment of injuries and illnesses and provide immediate life support and care before emergency medical service (EMS) professionals arrive.

All employees should know how to report injuries and call for emergency first aid assistance.

Where Are the Regulations?

The Occupational Safety and Health Administration's (OSHA) requirements for first aid are found in 29 CFR 1910.151. When there is no nearby infirmary, clinic, or hospital that can be used to treat injured employees, the employer must train persons to render first aid.

Roles of the First Aid Provider

The first aid provider is an important part of the EMS system. Designations of professional emergency medical care providers in the EMS system include: First Responder, Emergency Medical Technician (Basic and Intermediate), and Paramedic.

First aid providers:

- Take care of the safety of the overall scene — the ill/injured person, bystanders, and themselves.

- Safely gain access to the ill/injured person.

- Assess the ill/injured person to identify life-threatening conditions.

- Provide emergency care to the ill/injured person. (If the injured/ill person is responsive and alert, he or she must consent to receive first aid.)

- Turn over care to the EMS professionals.

Because of the stress and unpredictability involved in situations where an injury or illness has occurred, the first aid provider's first priority always must be the safety and well-being of the first aid provider.

First Aid Duties

First aid training should be conducted by qualified instructors. Trainees should have plenty of time to learn the material, ask questions, and practice first aid procedures.

In all cases involving serious injuries or illnesses, the most important first step in any first aid procedure is to call for EMS professionals.

Moving the Victim

The greatest danger in moving a victim is the possibility of aggravating a spine injury. An ill/injured person should be moved immediately only when there is an immediate danger to the person (fire, flood, collapse, etc.) or if life-saving care can't be given because of the person's location or position (a cardiac arrest victim sitting in a chair). If an emergency move is necessary, the first aid provider should provide as much protection to the spine as possible.

Cardiopulmonary Resuscitation and AEDs

First aid providers should receive specialized training in how to administer Cardiopulmonary Resuscitation (CPR). CPR is administered when an unconscious victim has no signs of heart activity, such as normal breathing, movement, or response to other stimulation. In CPR, the first aid provider uses techniques for artificial respiration and chest compressions.

Some employers have Automated External Defibrillators (AEDs) available in the workplace. First aid providers who have received specialized training in the use of AEDs can use them to help restore a normal heart rhythm through the application of an electric shock through the victim's chest wall.

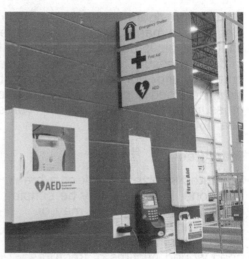

Burns

First aid providers should be trained to recognize the severity of burns.

First degree burns are the least severe — they result in redness or discoloration, mild swelling, and pain. A recommended treatment may be to immerse the area in cold water. Recommended treatment for chemical burns may include prompt flushing with plenty of clean water and removing contaminated clothing.

Second degree burns involve more tissue damage — they result in blisters, swelling, and pain. A recommended treatment may be to immerse the area in cold water and/or apply a cold, wet compress. Keeping the burned area elevated may help reduce swelling. Blisters should not be broken.

Third degree burns involve deeper tissue damage — the skin may look charred or white. Recommended first aid treatment may include covering the burned area with a sterile dressing and getting EMS assistance as quickly as possible.

Bleeding

First aid providers should be trained on how to help control bleeding. In many cases, the wounded part of the body should be elevated to help decrease blood flow to the area. In direct pressure, a compress is held with pressure directly on the wound. For severe bleeding, it may be necessary to slow the blood supply to the wounded area by applying pressure at a "pressure point" — pressing against an artery near the armpit or groin.

Fractures

Fractures involve a crack or a break in a bone. Fractures may be simple or compound. A fracture may or may not involve the bone penetrating the skin to cause an open wound. Victims of fractures may remember hearing a bone crack during the injury. The fracture will cause pain, movement of a joint or limb may be abnormal, and there may be swelling or noticeable deformities in the area. First aid providers should be trained to keep the patient stable, control severe bleeding, and immobilize the affected area without making the injury more severe.

Shock

A severe injury can cause the victim to go into shock — a condition where normal body functions are depressed. In early stages of shock, the victim may become pale, have a weak, rapid pulse, and have abnormal breathing. In advanced shock, the victim's blood pressure drops, body temperature falls, and the patient is in critical condition. First aiders need to be trained to recognize and treat shock. Recommended treatment may include covering the victim to maintain body temperature. It may also be beneficial to keep the patient lying down.

Other Injuries

A first aid provider can encounter many other injuries and illnesses. The information in this chapter is only meant to make you aware of the need to have first aid providers and to outline some of their responsibilities. Anyone who will be providing first aid needs thorough training.

Understand Bloodborne Pathogens

The bloodborne pathogens standard outlines practices to help protect workers from getting infections caused by germs carried in human blood. It applies to all employees that could be exposed to blood or other potentially infectious materials.

Where Are the Regulations?

OSHA regulations governing exposure to bloodborne pathogens are found in 29 CFR 1910.1030. It is the employer's responsibility to develop an exposure control plan; provide training to those workers potentially exposed to bloodborne pathogens as part of their job duties; implement engineering and work practice controls; enforce the use of personal protective equipment; offer a hepatitis B vaccine, exposure evaluation, and follow-up; and use signs and labels to warn of potential hazards.

If you are a health professional, a designated first aid provider in your company, or are involved in maintenance or housekeeping work where you could reasonably be expected to be exposed to bloodborne pathogens, you need to know about this standard.

"Good Samaritan" acts performed by undesignated employees are not covered by the standard, but undesignated first aid responders may want to know exposure controls anyway, to protect themselves if they voluntarily respond in the event of an emergency.

Key Definitions

Because of the technical nature of some of the words used when talking about bloodborne pathogens, some key definitions are spelled out here. Refer back to these definitions if you don't understand something later in this chapter.

Bloodborne Pathogens: Microorganisms present in human blood that can cause disease in humans. These include, but are not limited to, hepatitis B virus (HBV) and human immunodeficiency virus (HIV).

Exposure Incident: A specific eye, mouth, other mucous membrane, non-intact skin, or parenteral contact with blood or other potentially infectious material that results from doing one's job.

Occupational Exposure: A reasonably anticipated skin, eye, mucous membrane, or parenteral contact with blood or other potentially infectious material that may result from doing one's job.

Other Potentially Infectious Materials (OPIMs): Certain specific types of body fluids outlined in OSHA's standard, any body fluid that is visibly contaminated with blood, and all body fluids in situations where it is difficult or impossible to differentiate between body fluids.

Parenteral: A piercing of mucous membranes or the skin barrier by means of a needlestick, human bite, cut, and/or abrasion.

Universal Precautions: An infection control approach whereby all human blood and certain body fluids are treated as if they were known to be infectious for HIV, HBV, or other bloodborne pathogens.

Required Elements of the Standard

When workers are exposed to blood or OPIMs on the job, the standard requires that employers develop an exposure control plan.

Employers must also provide training on the following subjects to affected workers:

- Bloodborne diseases and how they are spread.

- The exposure control plan.

- Engineering and work practice controls.

- Personal protective equipment.

- Hepatitis B vaccine, exposure evaluation, and follow-up.

- How to respond to emergencies involving blood.

- Signs and labels used to warn of potential hazards.

Exposure Control Plan

While exposure control plans will vary from workplace to workplace, they have some common elements:

- Identification of job classifications and, in some cases, tasks where there is exposure to blood and other potentially infectious materials.

- A schedule of how and when the provisions of the standard will be implemented, including schedules and methods for communication of hazards to employees, hepatitis B vaccination and post-exposure evaluation and follow-up, recordkeeping, and implementation of:

  o Engineering and work practice controls.

- o Personal protective equipment.
- o Housekeeping.

- A description of how employees involved in direct patient care are involved in the selection of safer medical devices and other control measures.

- Procedures for evaluating the circumstances of an exposure incident.

The employer must keep the exposure control plan up to date.

Engineering Controls and Work Practices

The employer must also institute engineering controls and work practices that will minimize the possibility of exposure. Such things as handwashing, prevention of needlesticks, and minimization of the splashing or spraying of blood fall under this category. Engineering controls eliminate hazards at their source. This includes the use of autoclaves and containers for used sharps. Engineering controls must be checked and maintained on a regular schedule to keep them in good working order.

In the healthcare industry, employers must evaluate, select, and use appropriate safer medical devices, such as self-sheathing needles or needleless systems.

Employers must provide accessible facilities for handwashing. Wash hands immediately after removing gloves or other protective equipment, and after any hand contact with blood or OPIMs. If a sink isn't available for handwashing, antiseptic cleansers must be provided. In this case, wash with soap and water as soon as possible.

Do not bend, shear, break, remove or recap any used needle or sharp. Dispose of used sharps in the proper containers. These containers must be puncture resistant, be properly labeled, and have leakproof sides and bottoms.

Eating, drinking, applying cosmetics or lip balm, and handling contact lenses are prohibited in areas where there is a potential for exposure. Food or drink cannot be stored in refrigerators, freezers, shelves, cabinets or on counter tops where blood is stored or where blood or OPIMs may be present.

Personal Protective Equipment

Employers must provide, and employees must use, personal protective equipment (PPE) when the possibility exists for exposure to blood or OPIMs.

Personal protective equipment must be accessible and available in appropriate sizes. (Hypoallergenic or powderless gloves must be available to those allergic to regular gloves.) PPE must be kept clean and in good repair.

Single use gloves must be replaced as soon as possible after they are contaminated or if they become torn or punctured. These gloves should never be reused. Various other types of PPE include plastic visors, half-face masks, full body gown, goggles, etc.

Housekeeping Techniques

Housekeeping staff may be occupationally exposed to blood or OPIMs if they clean up after some first aid incidents. Therefore, housekeeping staff need to follow universal precautions and proper decontamination procedures.

Equipment and work areas must be cleaned and decontaminated as soon as feasible after contact with any blood or OPIMs.

Contaminated laundry should be handled as little as possible. Laundry must be bagged where it was contaminated. Wet laundry must be placed in leak-proof bags. All employees who handle contaminated laundry must wear gloves.

Hepatitis B Vaccine

A common bloodborne risk is infection by the hepatitis B virus. Because of this risk, your employer must make hepatitis B vaccine available to you when you are exposed to blood or OPIMs on the job.

Pre-screening cannot be done as a condition of receiving the vaccine. If you refuse to be vaccinated, you must sign a declination form. If you change your mind later on, your employer must still provide the vaccine.

Exposure Incident

An exposure incident is a specific work-related eye, mouth, other mucous membrane, non-intact skin, or parenteral contact with blood or OPIMs. When an exposure incident is reported, the employer will arrange for an immediate and confidential medical evaluation. The medical evaluation must:

- Document how the exposure occurred.
- Identify and test the source individual if feasible.
- Test the exposed employee's blood, if consent is obtained.
- Provide counseling.
- Evaluate, treat, and follow up on any reported illness.

Communication of Hazards

All warning labels must bear the biohazard symbol, be printed in fluorescent orange or orange-red, and have lettering of a contrasting color.

Red bags or containers may be used as a substitute for labels. Labels must be placed as close to the container as possible on all packages of regulated waste, refrigerators/freezers containing blood or OPIMs, and other containers used for shipping or storing blood and OPIMs.

Blood that has been tested and found free of HIV or HBV and released for clinical use and decontaminated regulated waste do not require labels.

Recordkeeping

The employer must keep records of employee training sessions for three years.

Under OSHA's rule for access to employee exposure and medical records (1910.1020), records must be maintained on all employees with occupational exposure.

Each record, which must be available to the employee, should include:

* Name and social security number.

* Hepatitis B vaccination status.

* Results of all exams, testing, and follow-up procedures.

* Copy of the healthcare professional's opinion.

* Copy of information provided to the healthcare professional.

These records are confidential and can be released only with the employee's written consent or if required by law.

Employers that must comply with OSHA's occupational injury and illness recordkeeping requirements (29 CFR Part 1904) must also keep a sharps injury log of percutaneous injuries from sharp materials that were contaminated with blood or OPIMs (i.e., needlestick injuries from used needles).

To protect yourself, follow the bloodborne pathogens exposure control plan your employer has set up.

Work at Working Safely

Everyone needs to know how to get emergency first aid assistance. You should understand that first aid providers:

1. Are designated by the employer and receive thorough training.
2. Take care of the safety of the injured person, bystanders, and themselves.
3. Safely gain access to the ill/injured person.
4. Assess the injuries/illness and provide emergency care.
5. Turn over care to the EMS professionals.

If you're a first aid provider, healthcare employee, a maintenance or janitorial person responsible for cleaning up blood or OPIMs, or any other potentially exposed employee, then you need to know about:

1. The written exposure control plan.
2. The training to be provided to you.
3. Engineering controls and work practices to minimize the chance of exposure.
4. Personal protective equipment.
5. Housekeeping techniques to protect you.
6. The hepatitis B vaccine you are entitled to.
7. The use of labeling and red bags to indicate contaminated waste.
8. Steps to be taken in the event of an exposure incident.

Safe at Home

It's just as important to have a well-stocked first aid kit at home as it is to have one available at work. Consider the types of injuries and illnesses your family may experience and match your supplies to those injuries. For example, if someone in your family has severe allergies, asthma, or other sudden-onset conditions, be ready with the proper medications. Take your first aid supplies with you when you travel, too

Be familiar with how to use your first aid supplies, and know their limitations. Make sure everyone in the family knows how to call for emergency medical assistance.

NOTES

Employee _____

Instructor _____

Date _____

Location _____

FIRST AID/BLOODBORNE PATHOGENS REVIEW

1. First aid providers:
   a. Can be anyone who first hears about an injury.
   b. Always continue to provide care after emergency medical service (EMS) professionals arrive.
   c. Perform an initial assessment of injuries and illnesses.
   d. Use complex, advanced medical equipment.

2. When there is no nearby clinic, infirmary, or hospital to treat injured employees:
   a. Employees may not do any hard work.
   b. Employees must have a buddy.
   c. An injured employee must treat his own injury.
   d. The employer must train persons to render first aid.

3. When a worker is injured, who is responsible for taking care of the safety of the overall scene?
   a. The injured worker.
   b. The first aid provider.
   c. The safety committee.
   d. The local police department.

4. The important first step for serious injuries and illnesses is to:
   a. Call for EMS professionals.
   b. Start cardiopulmonary resuscitation (CPR).
   c. Use an automated external defibrillator (AED).
   d. Move the victim.

5. If a first aid provider suspects that someone has fractured a bone, she will:
   a. Control severe bleeding.
   b. Immobilize the injury without making it worse.
   c. Keep the patient stable.
   d. All of the above.

6. First aid providers must be aware of practices to help workers from getting certain types of infections under OSHA's:
   a. First aid standard.
   b. Bloodborne pathogens standard.
   c. Hazard communication standard.
   d. Rules for emergency action plans.

7. Under the bloodborne pathogens standard, the employer isn't responsible for:
   a. Training employees potentially exposed to blood as part of their job duties.
   b. Developing an exposure control plan when employees have occupational exposure to blood.
   c. Training people who voluntary provide emergency help as a "Good Samaritan."
   d. Implementing engineering and work practice controls.

8. "Other potentially infectious materials (OPIMs)" include:
   a. Hazardous chemicals.
   b. Specific types of body fluids.
   c. Only body fluids that aren't visibly contaminated with blood.
   d. Any fluid.

9. If someone treats human blood and OPIMs as if they were known to be infectious:
   a. She must be a designated first aid provider.
   b. He is following "Universal Precautions."
   c. She never has occupational exposure to blood or OPIMs.
   d. He has parenteral contact.

10. Housekeeping staff who may be exposed to blood or OPIMs as part of the job:
    a. Must use universal precautions when they're occupationally exposed.
    b. Must find out who is the source of the blood or OPIMs.
    c. Must use safer medical devices.
    d. All of the above.

FOOT PROTECTION

The 26 bones in the foot are shaped in the form of an arch to provide a broad, strong support for the weight of the body. Because of how valuable our feet obviously are to us, we want to protect them from the hazards of the workplace.

Where Are the Regulations?

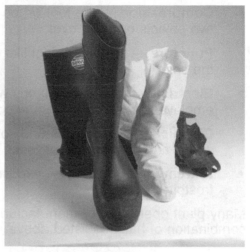

The Occupational Safety and Health Administration (OSHA) has developed regulations that specify foot protection to keep your feet safe at work. These regulations are located in 29 CFR 1910.132 and .136.

Your employer must assess the hazards in the workplace to determine if foot protection is needed.

Your employer must train you in the proper use of foot protection. You must know:

- When protective footwear is necessary.

- What footwear is necessary.

- How to properly put on, take off, adjust, and wear protective footwear.

- Protective footwear limitations.

- Proper care, maintenance, useful life, and disposal of protective footwear.

You must show you understand the training and can use safety shoes properly before you will be allowed to perform work requiring their use.

Some Types of Foot Injuries

Every day hundreds of workers in the United States suffer disabling injuries to their feet and toes. Yet many workers ignore the serious hazards in the workplace and refuse to wear protective footwear. Your feet are subject to cuts, punctures, burns, sprains, and fractures. But heavy objects falling or rolling onto the foot are the primary source of injury.

The hazards include:

- **Compression** — the foot or toe is squeezed between two objects or rolled over.

- **Puncture** — a sharp object like a nail breaks through the sole.

- **Electricity** — a hazard in jobs where qualified employees work on or near exposed energized parts.

- **Chemicals** — chemicals and solvents corrode ordinary shoes and can harm your feet.

- **Extreme heat or cold** — exposure can cause burns or frostbite.

Many plant operations or manufacturing processes involve a combination of hazards listed above.

Some Specific Types of Safety Shoes

Safety shoes come in many varieties to suit very specific industrial applications. Here are descriptions of some types of safety footwear.

Safety Shoes

Standard safety shoes have toes that meet standard testing requirements. Steel, reinforced plastic, and hard rubber are used for safety toes, depending on their intended use. These shoes are worn by workers in many types of general industry.

Metatarsal Guards

Shoes with metatarsal or instep
guards protect the upper foot from
impacts. In these shoes, metal
guards extend over the foot rather
than just over the toes.

Conductive Shoes

Conductive shoes permit the static
electricity that builds up in the
body of the wearer to drain off
harmlessly into the ground.

By preventing accumulation of static electricity, most
conductive shoes keep electrostatic discharge from igniting
sensitive explosive mixtures. These shoes are often worn by
workers in munitions facilities or refineries. Do not use these
shoes if you work near exposed electrical circuits.

Chemical-Resistant Safety Boots

Rubber or plastic safety boots offer protection against oil,
water, acids, corrosives, and other industrial chemicals. They
are also available with features like steel-toe caps, puncture-
resistant insoles, and metatarsal guards. Some rubber boots
are made to be pulled over regular safety shoes.

Electrical Hazard Shoes

Electrical hazard shoes offer insulation from electrical shock
hazards from contact with circuits of 600 volts or less under
dry conditions. These shoes are used in areas where
employees work on live or potentially live electrical circuits.
The toebox is insulated from the shoe so there is no exposed
metal. These shoes are most effective when dry and in good
repair.

Sole Puncture-Resistant Footwear

Puncture-resistant soles in safety shoes protect against
hazards of stepping on sharp objects that can penetrate
standard shoe soles. They are used primarily in construction
work.

Static Dissipative Shoes

Static dissipative footwear is designed to reduce accumulation of excess static electricity by conducting body charge to ground while maintaining some resistance to electrical shock. These shoes are worn by workers in the electronics industry where static could damage products.

Foundry Shoes

Foundry shoes are used by welders and molders in foundries or steel mills where there is a hazard from hot splashes of molten metal or flying sparks. Instead of laces, they have elastic gores to hold the top of the shoe close to the ankle. They can then be removed quickly in case hot metal or sparks get inside.

Add-On Foot Protection

Metatarsal guards and shoe covers can be attached to safety shoes or boots for greater protection from falling objects.

Rubber spats protect feet and ankles against chemicals. Puncture-proof inserts made of steel can be slipped into safety shoes or boots to protect against underfoot hazards. Strap-on cleats fastened to shoes can provide greater traction in ice or snow.

Be Sure Safety Footwear Meets Standards

OSHA regulations state
that safety footwear can
meet ANSI standards
(ANSI Z41-1991 or
ANSI Z41-1999).
However, ANSI Z41 has
been withdrawn. Two
ASTM standards, ASTM
F2412 and ASTM
F2413, have replaced

the former ANSI standard. OSHA regulations state that safety
footwear can meet ASTM F2412-2005 and ASTM F2413-
2005.

These standards set forth requirements for safety footwear in
the areas of electrical conductivity and resistance to impact,
compression, and puncture. You always want to match the
footwear to the job and its hazards.

Work at Working Safely

Safety shoes can prevent serious, even disabling, injuries at
relatively low cost. As a review, let's look at some of the
excuses that keep workers from using safety footwear. In
each case, we'll "stamp out" the excuse with the facts!

They're ugly! — Some people are willing to sacrifice safety
for style. However, safety shoes are now available in
fashionable styles ranging all the way from running shoes to
western boots.

They're too expensive! — When the cost is spread out over
the life of the shoe, the price of safety is only pennies a day.

They're not comfortable! — Safety shoes should fit just like
any other shoes.

They're too clumsy for climbing! — The key here is to find
a shoe suitable for working on ladders or scaffolding. Anyone
who works in those situations should wear a shoe with a
defined heel and good traction.

Steel toe caps will cut off my toes if crushed! — Toe caps are designed to give a "buffer zone" of space over the toes in case they are crushed.

I don't know where to buy them! — Some stores specialize in the sale of safety shoes. Shoemobiles, in-plant stores, and catalog order programs bring the shoes right to you on the job.

I'm a safe worker, I won't have an accident! — "It can't happen to me" is a dangerous myth that has been proven wrong again and again. So don't take a chance with your two good feet. Obtain proper safety footwear and wear it at all times on the job.

Safe at Home

Consider the need to wear protective footwear when you're off the job if you engage in activities that could cause foot injuries. For example, if you're doing home remodeling, moving stones for a landscaping project, or stacking firewood, you would benefit from the protection provided by safety shoes.

Even if you aren't doing anything that involves exposure to falling or crushing objects, be sure to wear sturdy footwear when you're doing activities such as operating a lawn mower, climbing a ladder, or walking where there might be sharp objects on the floor.

Employee _____

Instructor _____

Date _____

Location _____

FOOT PROTECTION REVIEW

1. Who must assess workplace hazards to determine if foot protection is needed?
   a. Each employee.
   b. The employer.
   c. OSHA.
   d. The insurance company.

2. You don't need to know about the limitations of protective footwear if you:
   a. Wore safety shoes on a previous job.
   b. Don't have any need to wear protective footwear.
   c. Wear electrical safety protective footwear.
   d. Aren't responsible for selecting protective footwear.

3. Before you can be allowed to perform work requiring protective footwear, you must:
   a. Remove all of the hazards from the work area.
   b. Try on at least three different styles of safety shoes.
   c. Show you understand your training and can properly use the protective footwear.
   d. Test the effectiveness of the protective footwear.

4. Some workplace hazards to the feet include:
   a. Punctures.
   b. Electricity.
   c. Chemicals.
   d. All of the above.

5. Conductive safety shoes:
   a. Are designed to protect you from electrical shocks.
   b. Cause electrical shocks.
   c. Prevent the accumulation of static electricity.
   d. Never protect from falling or crushing objects.

6. Employees who work on or near live or potentially live electrical circuits wear:
   a. Conductive shoes.
   b. Electrical hazard shoes.
   c. Metatarsal guards.
   d. None of the above.

7. Standard, non-specialized safety shoes:
   a. Have toes that meet standard testing requirements.
   b. Are the same as normal street-wear shoes.
   c. Are only available in one style.
   d. Can't use add-on metatarsal guards.

8. Foundry boots are designed so they:
   a. Can be removed quickly.
   b. Would only ever be worn by a foundry worker.
   c. Provide no toe protection from impact and compression.
   d. Must never include puncture-resistant soles.

9. Metatarsal guards:
   a. Protect the top of the foot from impacts.
   b. Protect the bottom of the foot from punctures.
   c. Provide extra electrical insulation.
   d. Must not be able to be removed from the shoe or boot.

10. Protective shoes:
    a. Are available from catalogs, stores, and other sources.
    b. Will cut off your toes if they're crushed.
    c. Are supposed to be uncomfortable.
    d. Are only available in one style.

FORKLIFT SAFETY

Driving a forklift is a serious responsibility. Consider that the average car weighs between 2,500 and 3,500 pounds. A forklift that is able to carry up to 6,000 pounds weighs two or three times as much. With a capacity load, you are handling a mass as high as 16,000 pounds.

Where Are the Regulations?

The Occupational Safety and Health Administration (OSHA) has issued regulations specifying general requirements for powered industrial trucks (OSHA's term for forklifts, platform lift trucks, motorized hand trucks, among others) safety and training. These regulations can be found in 29 CFR 1910.178.

Operators must successfully complete training and an evaluation of their skills.

The training covers safe operation of the type of truck that is being used, the hazards in the workplace, and OSHA's regulation.

Drivers will have refresher training and evaluations as needed. An evaluation of each operator's performance must be done at least every three years.

Forklifts: Basic Loading/Unloading Tools

Forklifts are powered by various means: gasoline or diesel fuel, propane gas, or electric power from batteries.

Lift trucks come with a number of specialized options, such as clamps, pole carriers, buckets, and swing arms. There are related lifters, such as pallet trucks, towing trucks, low lifters, and port-trucks. All require special training and knowledge of safe operation.

Forklifts Are Unique

Driving a forklift is a unique experience. Forklifts weigh much more than cars and are steered from the rear axle rather than the front as in a car. Rear wheel steering allows a forklift to turn in a tight radius, but it also means that the rear of a forklift will swing considerably wider than the rear of a car when turning.

Forklifts vs. Cars

Operating a forklift is fundamentally different from driving cars or other trucks. Be aware that a forklift:

- Steers more easily loaded than empty (because the load is balanced by counterweights).

- Is driven in reverse as often as forward.

- Is often steered with one hand.

- Has a center of gravity that is towards the rear and shifts toward the front as the forks are raised.

Cars use a four-point suspension system while forklifts use a three-point suspension. This system permits the center of gravity to shift in a forklift but makes it more likely to tip over.

Center of Gravity

The center of gravity for a forklift moves depending on the load and how it is positioned. The center of gravity will move when accelerating, braking, and turning. Therefore, it is very important to avoid quick accelerating or braking or turning a corner too fast.

Another factor that will affect the center of gravity is the load itself. Position the load close to the mast and tilted back. Tilting the mast back when traveling with a load creates better vehicle/load balance.

Never travel with the load elevated any more than is necessary to clear any bumps or curbs. On an incline of more than ten percent, drive with the load upgrade, forward up a ramp and reverse down a ramp.

Remember that these units are made to travel with loads. An unloaded forklift has the potential to tip because of the extreme weight of the counterbalance. Safe driving is just as important with an unloaded forklift as it is with one that is loaded.

Nameplates

Each manufacturer provides an identification plate, or nameplate, on every forklift they build. This plate gives you valuable information about the forklift's design and capacity. It tells you how much the unit weighs (important to know before you drive into a trailer or elevator) and how much it can carry.

Operating Your Forklift Safely

Start by getting into and out of your forklift properly. Use a three-point stance with two hands and one foot in contact with the floor or unit at all times. Never jump on or off the forklift.

Become familiar with all controls (both location and operation). Controls may vary from unit to unit. Be sure you understand every control on your forklift before you start it.

If the forklift has a seat belt, wear it! A seat belt will help to hold you in the frame of the safety cage should the vehicle tip. If you attempt to jump off the forklift, you are likely to be trapped under it or the load it's carrying.

The following "rules of the road" list general guidelines for safe forklift operations.

- Always keep arms and legs inside the vehicle.

- Face the direction of travel, and never travel forward with the load blocking your view.

- Keep three vehicle lengths following distance from other vehicles.

- No horse play is allowed. It's basic common sense.

- Be aware of overhead clearances, such as pipes, sprinklers, door beams, and know the load limits of elevators.

When picking up a load:

- Make sure the load does not exceed the capacity of your forklift.

- Make sure forks are positioned properly.

- Make sure the load is balanced and secure.

- Check for overhead obstructions.

- Raise the forks to the proper height.

- Bring the forks all the way into a pallet, and tilt the mast back to stabilize the load before moving.

- Back out, stop completely, then lower the load.

Traveling with a load:

- Pedestrians always have the right of way.

- Never allow anyone to ride on your forklift.

- When moving, always have the forks as low as possible, but high enough to clear bumps and curbs. Never travel with a load raised high.

- Know the position of your forks at all times.

- Keep the load tilted back slightly.

- Obey speed limits.

- Slow down at all intersections, and always sound the horn at blind corners.

- Always drive forward when going up ramps, and back up to go down ramps and inclines.

- Avoid sudden braking.

- Lift or lower the load only when completely stopped, never when traveling.

- Keep to the right, the same as highway driving with a car.

- Be alert for oil and grease spots, which could reduce traction.

- Make sure the load is balanced and secure on the forks.

- Cross railroad tracks at an angle, one wheel at a time.

- Be careful of changing light conditions, such as coming in from bright daylight into dimly lit areas, and vice-versa.

- Beware of edges on loading docks.

- Be very careful to watch your blind spots. Accidents involving forklifts that hit pedestrians and objects are far too common.

When placing a load:

- Stop the forklift completely before raising the load.

- Move slowly with the load raised.

- Never walk or stand under a raised load.

- Tilt the load forward only when over a stack or rack.

- Be certain the forks clear the pallet before turning or changing height after you've set down the load.

- Always stack the load square and straight.

- Before backing, check behind and on both sides for pedestrians or other traffic.

When you leave a forklift unattended, completely lower the load engaging means, neutralize controls, set the brakes to prevent movement, and shut off the power. **NOTE**: A powered industrial truck is unattended when the operator is 25 feet or more away from the vehicle which remains in his or her view, or whenever the operator leaves the vehicle and it is not in view.

If you get off the truck and stay within view and within 25 feet of it, you must still lower the forks, put the controls in neutral, and set the brakes; but you can leave the power on.

Fueling the Unit

Be sure to carefully follow the procedures set up for your lift trucks whether they are powered by propane, gasoline or diesel fuel, or batteries.

Vehicle Maintenance Is a Continual Job

Maintaining your forklift properly is just as important as driving safely. A regular maintenance schedule should be set up for forklifts, and you should always run down a safety checklist at the start of your shift. Any forklift not in safe operating condition must be removed from service.

Brakes

Push the brake pedal in. It should have free travel before meeting resistance. Then, depress the pedal again and hold it for ten seconds. The pedal must hold solid and not be spongy or drift under pressure. Make sure the parking brake and the seat brake on electric trucks are working properly. If the brakes are not working properly, the vehicle should not be driven.

Steering

Steering is a vital maintenance concern. With the engine running, check if the steering wheel turns correctly both ways to its stops. The wheel should not feel loose and the pump should not squeal before reaching the stops.

Inspection Checklist

Adhere to this checklist when you do an inspection:

- Check the fork pins and stops to make sure that they are in place.

- Check all cowling and body parts.

- Check the fuel level, crankcase oil level, radiator water level. Check the engine air cleaner, the fan belt, the hydraulic fluid level, and the battery water level.

- Check the hour meter and record it. This is important for maintenance scheduling.

- With the engine running, check operation of the hour meter, headlights, taillights, and warning lights.

- Check the oil pressure gauge, the water temperature, ammeter, and sound the horn. Note if the clutch is working properly. Check the hydraulic controls and any other controls on the lift system.

- Check the wheels and tires for excessive wear.

- Look for any broken or loosened parts.

Anything not up to par must be reported to your foreman at once.

Work at Working Safely

Remember, when
operating a forklift, all of
your attention must be
focused on what you
are doing.

1. Never park in front
   of fire equipment,
   doors, exits, or high
   traffic areas.

2. Do not pass another
   vehicle in narrow
   aisles.

3. Never smoke in fueling areas.

4. If you cannot see past a load in front, travel backwards,
   carefully.

5. Know the load capacity and limits of your vehicle. Also,
   stay within any elevator or floor load limits.

6. Never attempt to lift a load beyond the load limits of your
   forklift.

7. Do only maintenance or repair work that you are
   authorized to do. Leave the rest to maintenance
   personnel.

8. When leaving your vehicle, lower the forks, put the
   controls in neutral, set the brakes, block the wheels if on
   an incline, shut the power off, and remove the ignition key
   or connector plug.

Employee _____

Instructor _____

Date _____

Location _____

FORKLIFT SAFETY REVIEW

1. What does OSHA's forklift standard require of operators at least once every three years?
   a. A vision exam.
   b. A hearing test.
   c. A performance evaluation.
   d. An accident review.

2. Forklifts are steered:
   a. From the front axle.
   b. From the rear axle.
   c. From both the front and rear axles.
   d. Using the same method as a passenger car.

3. What shifts forward as a load is raised?
   a. The truck's center of gravity.
   b. The load.
   c. Specialized clamp attachments on the forks.
   d. The operator's seat.

4. To keep the center of gravity close to the truck:
   a. Raise the load so the forks are level with the operator's head.
   b. Accelerate quickly when turning a corner.
   c. Position the load close to the mast.
   d. Tilt the load slightly forward.

5. When travelling, raise the load so that it's:
   a. Only high enough to clear bumps, curbs, and other obstacles.
   b. Level with the operator's head.
   c. High enough so that pedestrians can easily see it.
   d. Still able to scrape the floor slightly.

6. If the forklift isn't carrying a load:
   a. Anyone can operate it.
   b. Safe driving procedures aren't very important.
   c. It's important to still use safe operating procedures.
   d. Always drive it in reverse.

7. If the forklift has a seat belt:
   a. Wear it!
   b. Wear it only if you'll be driving on rough terrain.
   c. Don't wear it if you need to get off and on the truck often.
   d. Don't change how another driver has it adjusted.

8. If you're following another forklift, keep a following distance of:
   a. One truck length.
   b. No more than two truck lengths.
   c. Three truck lengths.
   d. More than four truck lengths.

9. When placing a load onto racks:
   a. Raise the forks while you drive forward to approach the racks.
   b. Ask a spotter to stand under the forks to help you.
   c. Move slowly to position the raised load.
   d. Tilt the load forward as you raise it.

10. If the forklift's brakes aren't working properly:
    a. Drive slower.
    b. Drive in reverse.
    c. Don't raise the load.
    d. Don't operate the truck until the brakes are repaired.

HAND PROTECTION

How would you answer the question, "What is the most used tool in industry?" Some people would name a commonly used hand tool like a hammer or screwdriver. Others might respond with a list of larger equipment such as lathes or power tools. But the correct answer is deceptively simple. The most used tool in almost any workplace is the human hand.

Hand protection is important because our hands are exposed to so many hazards in the workplace.

Where Are the Regulations?

The Occupational Safety and Health Administration (OSHA) regulates personal protective equipment in general and hand protection at 29 CFR 1910.132 and .138. OSHA requires your employer to select and provide you with hand protection when you are exposed to hazards such as skin absorption of harmful substances, cuts or lacerations, abrasions, punctures, chemical burns, or harmful temperature extremes.

Your employer must assess the hazards in the workplace to determine if hand protection is needed.

Your employer must train you in the proper use of hand protection. You must know:

- When hand protection is necessary.

- What type is necessary.

- How to properly put on, take off, adjust, and wear gloves, mitts, or other protection.

- Hand protection limitations.

- Proper care, maintenance, useful life, and disposal of hand protection.

You must show that you understand the training and can use hand protection properly before you will be allowed to perform work requiring its use.

Hand Injuries Are Common

At work, your hands are exposed to three basic kinds of hazards:

- **Mechanical hazards**. These are present wherever machinery is used. Injuries resulting from machinery use might include cuts, punctures, abrasions, or crushing.

- **Environmental hazards**. Factors like extreme heat or cold, electricity, and materials handling have the potential to injure your hands.

- **Irritating substances**. Skin conditions such as dermatitis can be caused by contact with chemicals and biological agents (bacteria, fungi, and viruses). Chemicals and toxic substances can also enter the blood stream through abrasions or cuts.

The First Defense

The first defense in the battle to reduce hand injuries is engineering controls designed into equipment during manufacture or used to alter the work environment to make it safe. Machine guards protect hands and fingers from moving parts and should not be altered or removed.

Personal protective equipment (PPE) can help reduce the frequency and severity of hand and finger injuries.

Gloves

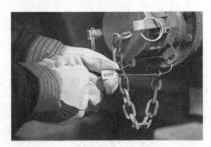

Gloves are perhaps the most commonly used type of PPE. They provide protection to fingers, hands, wrists, and forearms. Gloves should be selected to protect against specific hazards. Types range from common canvas work gloves to highly specialized gloves used in specific industries.

Leather

Leather gloves are useful for handling rough or abrasive materials. Leather gloves are also useful for handling hot objects.

Canvas

Canvas or cloth gloves are worn for general light-duty protection for handling rough objects.

Metal Mesh

Metal mesh gloves are worn by workers in the meat packing industry who work with sharp knives.

Chemical-Resistant

Rubber, vinyl, or neoprene gloves are used when handling caustic chemicals like acids, cleansers, or petroleum products. These gloves are rated as being safe for use with certain kinds of chemicals. For chemical-resistance information, read the glove manufacturer's chemical resistance charts. They rate each glove material and how it withstands specific chemicals.

Proper Fit Is Important

Wear only gloves that fit your hand. Gloves that are too small can tire your hands, and gloves that are too large are clumsy to work with. Gloves should be worn with great caution near moving equipment or machinery parts. The glove could get caught and pull your fingers or hand into the machinery. Gloves should be given proper care and cleaning. They should be inspected regularly for change in shape, hardening, stretching, or rips.

Work at Working Safely

Because you use your hands every day on the job, they can easily be injured. Keep these points in mind to protect your hands as you work:

1. Protective equipment selection depends upon the nature of the hazards in your workplace.

2. Gloves should fit you properly and be maintained in the same careful way as other safety equipment.

3. Do not wear gloves where they could get caught in moving machine parts.

Safe at Home

You can probably think of plenty of reasons to wear gloves to protect your hands at home. Here are a few examples:

- Any time you handle rough or sharp objects or use hand tools, you can help prevent abrasions, blisters, and cuts by wearing leather or canvas gloves.

- If your hands could get wet from cleaning products, paints, or other chemicals, you can keep from getting dry, cracked skin or chemical burns by wearing rubber gloves.

- Hand protection is even necessary for something as simple as taking a hot pan off of the stove. Using a pot holder prevents painful burns.

Employee _____

Instructor _____

Date _____

Location _____

HAND PROTECTION REVIEW

1. If your job exposes you to the risk for skin absorption of harmful substances:
   a. You need to wear hand protection.
   b. You can only work a limited number of hours.
   c. You should wash your hands only at the end of your shift.
   d. OSHA classifies it as a "high-hazard occupation."

2. If you need to wear hand protection, you must know:
   a. The limitations of the hand protection.
   b. The type of hand protection needed.
   c. When you need to wear the hand protection.
   d. All of the above.

3. You must show that you understand the limitations of the hand protection:
   a. Whenever you tear a glove.
   b. Every time you get a new pair of gloves.
   c. Before you're allowed to do work that requires the use of hand protection.
   d. All of the above.

4. Three basic types of hazards to the hands are:
   a. Abrasions, environmental hazards, and irritating substances.
   b. Mechanical hazards, extreme heat, and irritating substances.
   c. Mechanical hazards, environmental hazards, and liquids.
   d. Mechanical hazards, environmental hazards, and irritating substances.

5. Methods to reduce the risk of hand injuries:
   a. Are called "engineering controls."
   b. Can include designing equipment to make it safe.
   c. Can include altering the work environment to make it safe.
   d. All of the above.

6. Gloves:
   a. May be the most commonly used type of personal protective equipment (PPE).
   b. Do nothing to reduce the frequency of hand and finger injuries.
   c. Don't need to be selected for protection against specific hazards.
   d. Are the only method to reduce the risk of hand injuries.

7. What type of glove is color-coded to show its level of protection?
   a. Metal mesh.
   b. Electrical-resistant.
   c. Canvas.
   d. Leather.

8. Electrical-resistant and chemical-resistant gloves can both be made from:
   a. Leather.
   b. Fabric.
   c. Rubber.
   d. Metal mesh.

9. What type of glove is typically used by workers who handle sharp knives?
   a. Impact-resistant.
   b. Impervious.
   c. Metal mesh.
   d. Conductive.

10. What types of gloves are used to handle rough materials or objects?
    a. Leather or rubber.
    b. Leather or electrical-resistant.
    c. Chemical-resistant or metal mesh.
    d. Leather or canvas.

HAZARD COMMUNICATION

If you come into contact with hazardous chemicals in your workplace each day, you are definitely not alone. Many people are exposed to hazardous chemicals on the job. In many cases, the chemicals you deal with may be no more dangerous than those you use at home. But in the workplace, concentrations are likely to be higher and exposure time longer. Thus, potential hazards are greater on the job.

Where Are the Regulations?

The Occupational Safety and Health Administration (OSHA) has issued a regulation to help you learn about the hazards of the chemicals you use on the job. The regulation is called the hazard communication standard, but is more commonly called "HazCom" or the "Right to Know Law." It can be found at 29 CFR 1910.1200. A 2012 revision aligns the regulation with the United Nations' Globally Harmonized System of Classification and Labeling of Chemicals (GHS).

The standard says you have a right to know what chemicals you are working with or around. You also have a right to understand the hazards.

The HazCom standard requires that all chemicals in your workplace be classified for potential hazards. And, it mandates that information relating to these hazards be made available to you.

The areas specifically covered in the standard include:

- Classifying the hazards of chemicals.
- Safety data sheets (SDSs).
- Labels and labeling.
- A written hazard communication program.

- Employee information and training.
- Trade secrets.

The HazCom standard doesn't apply to hazardous waste/ substances regulated by the Environmental Protection Agency, biological hazards, tobacco products, many wood or wood products, or to food, cosmetics, or certain drugs.

What Are Hazardous Chemicals?

A *hazardous chemical* is any substance classified as:

- A physical hazard.
- A health hazard.
- A simple asphyxiant.
- Combustible dust.
- Pyrophoric gas.
- Another hazard not otherwise classified.

What Are Physical Hazards?

Physical hazards are chemicals that are classified as posing one or more of the following hazardous effects:

- Explosive.
- Flammable gases, aerosols, liquids, or solids.
- Oxidizer (liquid, solid, or gas).
- Self-reactive.
- Pyrophoric (liquid or solid).
- Self-heating.
- Organic peroxide.
- Corrosive to metal.

- Gas under pressure.
- Emits flammable gas when in contact with water.

In addition, a pyrophoric gas is a chemical in a gaseous state that will ignite spontaneously in air at a temperature of 130 degrees F (54.4 degrees C) or below.

You should also be aware that some dusts can be combustible in some situations. Substances that can create combustible dusts when they are processed could include:

- Grains, sugar, and other types of food and agricultural products.
- Charcoal, soot, and similar materials.
- Chemicals, such as sulfur.
- Metals, such as magnesium or aluminum.
- Plastics and resins.

A spark or flame can cause a combustible dust fire or explosion if, for example, a build-up of the dust is disturbed so that the dust is suspended in the air in a confined area.

What Are Health Hazards?

Health hazards are chemicals that are classified as posing one or more of the following hazardous effects:

- Acute toxicity from any route of exposure (e.g., ingestion, inhalation, etc.).
- Skin corrosion or irritation.
- Serious eye damage or eye irritation.
- Respiratory or skin sensitization (e.g., an allergic reaction).
- Aspiration hazard.
- Carcinogenicity.
- Reproductive toxicity.
- Germ cell mutagenicity.
- Specific target organ toxicity from a single or repeated exposure (e.g., a chemical that can damage the liver).

In addition, a simple asphyxiant is a substance or mixture that displaces oxygen in the air to create an oxygen-deficient atmosphere that can lead to unconsciousness and death.

Some of these health hazards can occur rapidly, following a brief exposure (an acute effect). Health hazards can also cause long-term effects that usually follow repeated long-term exposure (a chronic effect).

The Safety Data Sheet

You can find detailed information about a chemical's hazards on its SDS. An SDS is a fact sheet for a hazardous chemical. SDSs must be in English and contain the following sections in the order listed:

- **Section 1, Identification** includes product identifier; manufacturer or distributor name, address, phone number; emergency phone number; recommended use; restrictions on use.

- **Section 2, Hazard(s) identification** includes all hazards regarding the chemical; required label elements.

- **Section 3, Composition/information on ingredients** includes information on chemical ingredients; trade secret claims.

- **Section 4, First aid measures** includes important acute or delayed symptoms/effects; required treatment.

- **Section 5, Fire-fighting measures** lists suitable extinguishing techniques/equipment; chemical hazards from fire.

- **Section 6, Accidental release measures** lists emergency procedures; protective equipment; proper methods of containment and cleanup.

- **Section 7, Handling and storage** lists precautions for safe handling and storage, including incompatibilities.

- **Section 8, Exposure controls/personal protection** lists OSHA's Permissible Exposure Limits (PELs); Threshold Limit Values (TLVs); appropriate engineering controls; personal protective equipment (PPE).

- **Section 9, Physical and chemical properties** lists the chemical's characteristics.

- **Section 10, Stability and reactivity** lists chemical stability and possibility of hazardous reactions.

- **Section 11, Toxicological information** includes routes of exposure; related symptoms, acute and chronic effects; numerical measures of toxicity.

- **Section 12, Ecological information**.

- **Section 13, Disposal considerations**.

- **Section 14, Transport information**.

- **Section 15, Regulatory information**.

- **Section 16, Other information** includes the date of preparation or last revision.

The SDS must be in English, but the employer may have copies in other languages as well. The SDS will indicate if there is no relevant information available within a Section. OSHA does not enforce Sections 12 through 15, so an SDS may not have complete information in these sections.

Your organization must have an SDS for each hazardous chemical it uses. Copies must be kept where you can use them during your work shift. When employees must travel between workplaces during the day, SDSs may be kept at a central location.

Material safety data sheets (MSDS) were required before OSHA issued the SDS requirements in March 2012. Until chemical manufacturers and importers convert MSDSs to the SDS format, you will still see MSDSs in use. MSDSs must contain the following information, but the information does not need to be in this order:

- Identity of the chemical (as used on the label).

- Physical and chemical characteristics (e.g., vapor pressure, flash point).

- Physical hazards.
- Health hazards.
- Primary routes of entry.
- PELs, TLVs , or other exposure limits used or recommended by the MSDS preparer.
- Whether the chemical is a carcinogen.
- Precautions for safe handling and use.
- Control measures (e.g., engineering controls, work practices).

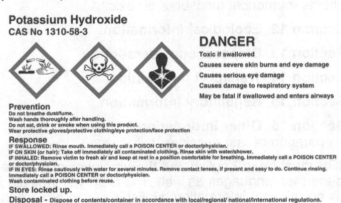

Potassium Hydroxide
CAS No 1310-58-3

DANGER

Toxic if swallowed
Causes severe skin burns and eye damage
Causes serious eye damage
Causes damage to respiratory system
May be fatal if swallowed and enters airways

Prevention
Do not breathe dust/fume.
Wash hands thoroughly after handling.
Do not eat, drink or smoke when using this product.
Wear protective gloves/protective clothing/eye protection/face protection

Response
IF SWALLOWED: Rinse mouth. Immediately call a POISON CENTER or doctor/physician.
IF ON SKIN (or hair): Take off immediately all contaminated clothing. Rinse skin with water/shower.
IF INHALED: Remove victim to fresh air and keep at rest in a position comfortable for breathing. Immediately call a POISON CENTER or doctor/physician.
IF IN EYES: Rinse cautiously with water for several minutes. Remove contact lenses, if present and easy to do. Continue rinsing. Immediately call a POISON CENTER or doctor/physician.
Wash contaminated clothing before reuse.

Store locked up.

Disposal - Dispose of contents/container in accordance with local/regional/ national/international regulations.

Chemicals USA • 1234 Dangerous Rd. • Allendale, NJ 07401

Labels and Labeling Requirements

The chemical manufacturer, importer, or distributor must make sure that each container of hazardous chemicals leaving the workplace is labeled, tagged, or marked with the following information:

- **Product identifier**. This is the name or number used to identify the chemical. It will also be used to identify the chemical on the SDS and the list of hazardous chemicals in the employer's written hazard communication program.

- **Signal word**. This helps you know how severe the hazard is. The word "danger" is used for the more severe hazards, and "warning" is used for the less severe hazards.

- **Hazard statement.** This is a brief statement for a hazard class and category to describe the nature of the hazard.

- **Pictogram.** This is a symbol used to show you the chemical's hazard class. There are eight pictograms used to meet the HazCom standard's labeling requirements.

- **Precautionary statement.** This recommends the steps you should take to safely use, handle, and store the chemical.

- **Name, address, and telephone number** of the chemical manufacturer, importer, or other responsible party. The responsible party is someone who can provide more information on the chemical and what to do in case of an emergency.

The eight hazard symbol pictograms used for HazCom labels are:

- Flame.

- Flame over circle.

- Exclamation mark.

- Exploding bomb.

- Corrosion.

- Gas cylinder.

- Health hazard.

- Skull and crossbones.

Flame is used for:

- Flammables.

- Pyrophorics.

- Self-heating.

- Emits flammable gas.

- Self-reactives.

- Organic peroxides.

Flame over circle is used for:

- Oxidizers.

Exploding bomb is used for:

- Explosives.
- Self-reactives.
- Organic peroxides.

Gas cylinder is used for:

- Gases under pressure.

Corrosion is used for:

- Skin corrosion; burns.
- Eye damage.
- Corrosive to metals.

Exclamation mark is used for:

- Irritant (skin and eye).

- Skin sensitizer.
- Acute toxicity (harmful).
- Narcotic effects.
- Respiratory tract irritant.

Health hazard is used for:

- Carcinogenicity.
- Respiratory sensitizer.
- Reproductive toxicity.
- Target organ toxicity.
- Mutagenicity.
- Aspiration toxicity.

Skull and crossbones is used for:

- Acute toxicity (fatal or toxic; severe).

You might also see GHS labels using an **Environmental** pictogram to show aquatic toxicity hazards. OSHA's HazCom standard doesn't require the use of the Environmental pictogram.

Until chemical manufacturers, importers, or distributors revise container labels to show the pictograms and other hazard classification information required by OSHA's March 2012 revision to the HazCom standard, you will still see incoming containers with labels that only have the following information on them:

- Identity of the hazardous chemical.

- Appropriate hazard warnings.

- Name and address of the chemical manufacturer, importer, or other responsible party.

All container labels must be in English, but information may also be presented in other languages for non-English speaking employees.

Containers of hazardous chemicals that have been shipped to your workplace arrive with the labels already on them. As you use the chemical in the workplace, you can rely on the labels that were on the containers when they arrived. OSHA does not require containers to be re-labeled (unless a label falls off a container or if it becomes unreadable).

Some employers opt to use a different labeling system, such as the Hazardous Material Information System (HMIS), to label in-house workplace containers of hazardous chemicals. OSHA does not require any particular system to be used when re-labeling in-house workplace containers, but the labels must include:

- The product identifier.

- Words, pictures, symbols, or a combination of these, that provide at least general information on the hazards of the chemicals. These hazard warnings must be able to be used along with the SDSs and other information immediately available to employees under the hazard communication program so that workers have specific information on the chemical's physical and health hazards.

On individual stationary containers, such as a tank, you may use signs, placards, batch tickets, or printed operating procedures in place of labels. These signs, etc., must include the same information as would be on a label.

Some items do not need to be labeled. Pipes or piping systems, and engines, fuel tanks, or other operating systems in a vehicle, are not considered to be containers, so they do not need to be labeled. Also, if you transfer a chemical from a labeled container into a portable container for your own immediate use during your shift, you are not required to label the container; however, it 's always a good practice to identify the contents of any container.

The Written Hazard Communication Program

Your employer is required by the HazCom standard to have developed and implemented a written hazard communication program.

Your organization's written program needs to include:

- A list of the hazardous chemicals known to be present in your workplace.

- How the SDS requirements are being met.

- What type of labeling system is used.

- Detailed information on training compliance.

- Methods your employer will use to inform you of the hazards of non-routine tasks and such things as unlabeled piping.

- Methods your organization will use to inform other employers of workers on your site, such as service representatives, repairmen, and subcontractors.

You Must Be Trained

You must be trained at the time of your initial employment or assignment, as well as whenever a new chemical hazard is introduced into your work area.

Your training must contain all of the following elements:

- **Methods or observations** used to detect the presence or release of hazardous chemicals in your work area.

- **The physical, health, simple asphyxiation, combustible dust, and pyrophoric gas hazards** of chemicals in your work area, as well as any chemical hazards not otherwise classified.

- **Measures you can take to protect yourself** from hazards, including work practices and personal protective equipment.

- **Details of your employer's hazard communication program**, including complete information on labels and SDSs.

Work at Working Safely

Take your HazCom training seriously. Learn about SDSs, labeling, your employer's written program, measures to protect yourself, and what hazardous chemicals you work with.

Safe at Home

You probably use cleaning supplies, paints, adhesives, pesticides, or other chemicals off the job, too. It's always a good practice to know the hazards of any product that contains chemicals.

Read the label when you buy a chemical product. Check the labels on similar products to see if they might be safer to use. You'll have fewer hazardous chemicals at home if you try to buy safer chemical products as you shop.

As you use chemicals at home:

- Follow all of the precautions on the label.

- Make sure there are no sources of sparks, heat, or flame in the area if you're using a chemical that can catch fire.

- Try to use as little of the chemical as you can to limit your exposure.

- Pay attention to the ventilation in the room, and keep doors and windows open to help keep the air moving.

- Consider wearing protective gear such as goggles and rubber gloves. Most hardware stores sell PPE.

- Plan ahead so you're ready to handle a spill.

- The product's label may have important information on signs and symptoms of overexposure. If you get a burn or begin to feel ill, stop using the chemical and get medical attention.

- Clean up right away when you're done, and wash carefully with warm soap and water after you use a chemical.

- Be sure to follow the recommendations for safe storage.

- Keep the chemical in its original container so the label information is always available. If you do have to transfer a chemical into another container, write the contents on it. It's a good practice to never use a food or beverage container. You don't want to risk someone mistaking a bottle with chemicals in it for a bottle of water. Or, when the job is done, you don't want to mistakenly put food or drink into a container that used to have chemicals in it.

Always keep chemicals out of the reach of children. If someone does accidently ingest a chemical, call immediately to get emergency medical assistance, and be prepared to provide the emergency responders with as much information as you can about the chemical.

NOTES

Employee _____

Instructor _____

Date _____

Location _____

HAZARD COMMUNICATION REVIEW

1. The HazCom standard requires chemicals to be:
   a. Classified for potential hazards.
   b. Identified using placards.
   c. Stored in locked closets.
   d. Regulated by the EPA.

2. The HazCom standard doesn't require labeling for:
   a. Hazardous waste regulated by the EPA.
   b. Piping systems.
   c. Fuel tanks in a vehicle.
   d. All of the above.

3. Which of the following is not a hazard symbol pictogram?
   a. Flame.
   b. Skull and crossbones.
   c. Question mark.
   d. Exclamation mark.

4. What is the same on the SDS, the list of hazardous chemicals, and the label?
   a. The emergency contact name.
   b. The product identifier.
   c. The precautionary statement.
   d. The PPE recommendations.

5. A flammable liquid is a:
   a. Sensitizer.
   b. Peroxide.
   c. Physical hazard.
   d. Health hazard.

6. A chemical that can cause serious eye irritation:
   a. Is not otherwise classified.
   b. Is a health hazard.
   c. Is corrosive to metal.
   d. Is self-reactive.

7. A safety data sheet (SDS):
   a. Must include the sections in the correct order.
   b. Can have the sections in any order.
   c. Must include only sections one through five.
   d. Must include photos and pictograms.

8. Copies of SDSs:
   a. Must be attached to each chemical container.
   b. Must be posted near the exits.
   c. Must be locked in the manager's office.
   d. Must be kept where workers can use them.

9. The signal word on the label:
   a. Is either "danger" or "warning."
   b. Is shown inside of a red diamond.
   c. Describes how you should use and store the chemical.
   d. None of the above.

10. The exclamation point pictogram is used to show that a chemical is:
    a. A skin or eye irritant.
    b. A respiratory tract irritant.
    c. A skin sensitizer.
    d. Any of the above.

HEAD PROTECTION

Head injuries can be minor or deadly. Injuries can include minor abrasions, concussions, lacerations, fractures, burns, or even electrocution.

Where Are the Regulations?

Head protection regulations for general industry are found in 29 CFR 1910.132 and .135. The standards recognized by OSHA for the design, construction, and use of protective headwear are in the American National Standard Institute's standard, ANSI Z89.1: *American National Standard for Industrial Head Protection*.

Your employer must assess the hazards in the workplace to determine if head protection is needed.

You must receive training in the proper use of head protection and understand the following concepts:

- When head protection is necessary.

- What type of head protection is necessary.

- How to properly put on, take off, adjust, and wear head protection.

- Limitations of head protection.

- Proper care, maintenance, useful life, and disposal of head protection.

You must show that you understand the training and can use head protection properly before you will be allowed to perform work requiring its use.

How Do Hard Hats Help?

Head injuries are caused by falling or flying objects or by bumping your head against a fixed object. Other causes are from electrical shock and burns. Hard hats are designed to do two things: resist the penetration and absorb the shock from a blow, and to provide protection from electrical shock and burn.

Hard hats lessen injury because the hard outer shell and the inner suspension system work together to absorb impacts. Hard hats that protect against electrical hazards are constructed of electrically insulating materials.

When to Use Hard Hats

When you are working in an area where there is a possible danger of head injury from impact from falling or flying objects, or where there is a risk of electrical shock and burns, you must wear your hard hat.

Types of PPE for the Head

Hard hats fall into two types and three classes in ANSI Z89.1. All types protect from falling objects. The classes are intended to provide protection against a specific hazardous condition.

The types include:

- Type 1 — intended to reduce the force of impact resulting from a blow only to the top of the head.

- Type 2 — intended to reduce the force of impact resulting from a blow which may be received off center or to the top of the head.

The classes of hard hats are:

* Class G — (General) low voltage protection.
* Class E — (Electrical) high voltage protection.
* Class C — (Conductive) no voltage protection.

Class G

These hard hats are used for protection against the force of impact and penetration by falling objects. They also reduce the danger from low-voltage exposures.

Class E

This type of hard hat protects your head from the force of impact and penetration by falling objects. It also offers protection from exposure to high-voltage.

Class C

The design of these hard hats offers protection from the force of impact and penetration by falling objects. They are used where there is no danger from electrical hazards.

Each approved hard hat is marked on the inside of the shell with the manufacturer's name, the applicable ANSI designation, and the Class.

Some helmets are designed so they accept attachments such as face shields, hearing protection, winter liners, or lamps. If accessories are not used properly, the hard hat may not provide as much protection. Always follow the manufacturer's instructions.

Work at Working Safely

You should take proper care of your hard hat to prolong its life and your safety. The safety provided by a hard hat is limited if it is damaged or if it is not used as it was intended to be used.

1. Check your hard hat daily for signs of dents, cracks, or penetration. Do not use the helmet if any of these signs of damage are found. This inspection should include the shell, suspension, headband, sweatband, and any accessories.

2. Do not store or carry your hard hat on the rear-window shelf of a car. Sunlight and high heat can degrade the helmet. Long periods of exposure to sunlight can lead to damage from ultraviolet rays. Signs of damage include a dulling, chalking, crazing, or flaking on the surface of the shell.

3. Clean your hard hat in warm, soapy water. Scrub and rinse the shell with clear, hot water (about 140 degrees F). Inspect the shell for damage after it has been cleaned.

4. Do not paint your hard hat. Some types of paint and thinners may damage the shell or weaken the helmet. Consult with the hard hat's manufacturer for recommendations on using any type of solvent to clean paint, tars, oils, or other materials from the helmet.

Safe at Home

You might think the last thing you'd ever do would be to wear a hard hat at home, but there are some situations when wearing head protection is a good idea. A hard hat can protect you from being injured by falling objects or by hitting your head on fixed objects if you need to:

- Prune trees.

- Work on the ground while someone is up doing roof repairs.

- Work under someone who is doing home repairs or remodeling while up on a scaffold or ladder.

- Work in tight areas such as a crawlspace or attic.

NOTES

Employee _____

Instructor _____

Date _____

Location _____

HEAD PROTECTION REVIEW

1. What type of injuries does head protection help prevent?
    a. Concussions.
    b. Electrocution.
    c. Lacerations.
    d. All of the above.

2. What must the employer do to determine if head protection is needed?
    a. Assume that all employees must wear hard hats at all times.
    b. Assess the hazards in the workplace.
    c. Let each employee decide whether or not to wear a hard hat.
    d. Require the use of hard hats only after there's been a serious injury.

3. Each worker who wears head protection must know:
    a. The industry's fatality rate for head injuries
    b. The details of the tests used to approve hard hats.
    c. When head protection is necessary.
    d. The most frequent type of head injuries for the industry.

4. Training on head protection must include:
    a. The proper care of the head protection.
    b. The proper maintenance of the head protection.
    c. The useful life of the head protection.
    d. All of the above.

5. Hard hats are designed to:
    a. Resist the penetration of only sharp objects.
    b. Absorb the shock from the impact of a blow only from the side of the head.
    c. Provide protection from electrical shock and burn.
    d. Protect from only small falling objects, such as pebbles.

6. What works together to absorb impacts?
   a. The employer and the employee.
   b. The hard hat and the head.
   c. The hard outer shell and the inner suspension system.
   d. The falling object and the hard hat.

7. Electrically insulating materials are used to make hard hats that:
   a. Protect against electrical hazards.
   b. Are approved for use during thunder storms.
   c. Provide protection from extreme cold temperatures.
   d. Dissipate static.

8. New hard hats are rated using the following classifications:
   a. Class A, Class B, and Class C.
   b. Class G, Class E, and Class C.
   c. Class A and Class C only.
   d. Class D, Class E, and Class F.

9. The inside of approved hard hats is marked with:
   a. The serial number and expiration date.
   b. The date of manufacture, the Type, and the Class.
   c. The manufacturer's name, address, and phone number.
   d. The manufacturer's name, the applicable ANSI designation, and the Class.

10. All Class C hard hats provide:
    a. No voltage protection.
    b. A little voltage protection.
    c. Medium voltage protection.
    d. The most voltage protection.

HEARING CONSERVATION

In the past, workers accepted partial hearing loss as a cost of working in a noisy plant. New workers were told by old-timers that they would soon get used to the noise. But times have changed. Noise is now recognized as an occupational hazard that can cause temporary or permanent hearing loss, stress, and other physical problems.

Where Are the Regulations

Regulations governing the allowable levels of noise and hearing protection requirements for employers to provide employees have been issued by the Occupational Safety and Health Administration (OSHA). The regulations can be found at 29 CFR 1910.95.

How Do We Hear?

A sound source sends out vibrations into the air. These vibrations are called sound waves. The ear changes the energy in sound waves into nerve impulses which travel to the brain and are then interpreted.

Sound is measured by its frequency and intensity. Frequency is the pitch (high or low) of a sound. High-frequency sound can be more damaging to your hearing than low-frequency sound. Intensity is the loudness of a sound. Loudness is measured in decibels (dB).

Intensity that exceeds an average of 85 dB over an eight-hour day may cause hearing loss. According to OSHA standards, employers must provide hearing protection when workers are exposed to noise at levels of 85 dB or more averaged over an eight-hour period.

Different Kinds of Noise

In general, there are three types of noise:

- Wide band is noise that is distributed over a wide range of frequencies. Examples are the noise produced in most manufacturing settings and by the operation of most internal combustion engines.

- Narrow band noise is restricted to a narrow range of frequencies. Examples include noise from various kinds of power tools, circular saws, fans, and planers.

- Impulse noise is composed of temporary "beats" that can occur in on-and-off repeating patterns. Jack hammers, or power or punch presses are good examples of tools that cause impulse noise.

How Does Noise Hurt?

How you're affected by noise depends on several things — loudness and frequency, length of exposure, and even your age and health.

A temporary hearing loss can occur from a short exposure to loud noise, but your hearing soon recovers when the noise stops. If the level is high enough for long enough, it can cause permanent hearing loss.

Hearing loss due to noise in the workplace is frequently ignored because it usually takes place over a long period of time and may not be readily apparent until the damage is done. There's no visible wound or other sign of injury.

But, too much noise can cause a variety of problems. It can make you tired and irritable from the strain of talking or trying to listen over loud sounds. You might not be able to hear important work or safety instructions because of excessive noise.

Evidence exists that other physical damage may occur because of the way the body reacts to noise.

Studies link noise with high blood pressure, ulcers, headaches, and sleeping disorders. Add these potential dangers to the obvious damage that noise can do to hearing.

Noise Can Be Controlled

If the noise level in your work area is too high, your employer must take additional action to reduce that noise. Steps to reduce noise might include:

- Moving noisy machinery to a separate area away from as many workers as possible, or building a sound barrier around it.

- Placing machinery on rubber mountings to reduce vibration.

- Using sound-absorbing acoustical tiles and blankets on floors, walls, and ceilings.

- Arranging work schedules to cut down on the time each worker spends in a noisy area.

Equipment manufacturers can also design quieter machinery.

However, if workers are still exposed to hazardous levels of noise after controls have been put in place, employers must provide hearing protective devices.

Protect Your Hearing

Various kinds of hearing protective devices are available for use in the workplace. The selection of the right hearing protection depends on several factors:

The noise hazard — what noise levels will you be dealing with?

Frequency of the noise — will it be low pitch or high pitch? (Some earplugs or muffs reduce the force of noise (attenuate) better at lower frequencies than at the higher frequencies.)

Fit and comfort — the protective devices must fit properly and be comfortable enough to wear as long as they are needed.

Noise Reduction Rating or NRR — all hearing protectors carry a label indicating the NRR; a higher number on the label means more effectiveness.

Types of Hearing Protection

Your employer will determine what types of hearing protection devices (HPDs) are needed.

Hearing protectors do not block out sound completely, but they reduce the amount of sound reaching the delicate parts of the ear. By doing so, they offer some protection.

Enclosure

The enclosure type of hearing protection completely surrounds the head like an astronaut's helmet. This type of protection is not too popular due to its cost and discomfort.

Earplugs

Earplugs fit in the ear canal. They come in three forms:

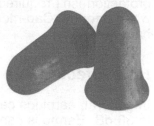

- **Custom-molded** earplugs are made for specific individuals, molded to the exact shape of that person's ear. Made from soft silicone ruber or plastic, they are reusable.

- **Molded inserts** often called pre-molded, are also made from soft silicone rubber or plastic. They are reusable and should be kept very clean. Use warm, soapy water to clean them after each use, rinse off the soap, and store them in a clean carrying case.

- **Formable** plugs are usually made of foam rubber; they are disposable.

Canal Caps

Canal caps (also known as superaural) seal the external edge of the ear canal to reduce sound. The caps are made of a soft, rubber-like substance and are held in place by a headband. This type of ear protection is a good alternative for those who can't use earplugs or for workers who enter and leave high noise areas frequently during the course of their work day.

Earmuffs

Earmuffs (also known as circumaural) fit over the whole ear to seal out noise. A typical muff is made up of three basic parts — cups, cushions, and headband. The cups are made of molded plastic and are filled with foam or other material. They vary in size and are adjustable. The cushions are covered with plastic and filled with liquid, air, or foam. The headband simply holds the cups against the head. It may be worn over the head, behind the neck, or under the chin.

There are also specialty earmuffs for different job requirements. Dielectric muffs have no metal parts for those workers exposed to high voltages. Electronic earmuffs reduce hazardous noise but magnify wanted sounds like voices.

Folding earmuffs are designed for use in situations where protection isn't required full-time but must be quickly available when needed. Cap-mounted muffs are attached directly to hard hats.

How Effective Are They?

In general, earplugs can reduce noise reaching the ear by 25 to 30 dB. Earmuffs can reduce noise 20 to 25 dB. Combinations of the two protectors can give 3 to 5 dB more protection. No matter what type of protection device you select, remember that the only effective hearing protector is the one that you wear!

Audiometric Testing Is Vital

It is very important to keep track of your hearing by having it tested periodically. An audiometric test is a procedure for checking a person's hearing. Employers with facilities where noise exposure equals or exceeds an average of 85 dBA over an eight-hour day are required to provide their employees with audiometric testing.

A trained technician uses an instrument (an audiometer) to send sounds (tones) through headphones. The person being tested responds to the test sounds when they are first heard. The chart that records responses to the test sounds is called an audiogram.

This test checks hearing ability so that any hearing loss can be identified and dealt with properly and promptly.

Work at Working Safely

You are ultimately responsible for protecting your own hearing. You have the most to lose if you suffer hearing loss as a result of on-the-job noise hazards. Let's review a few important reminders about hearing conservation:

1. Disposable earplugs may be more convenient to use than long-term use plugs, but make sure they fit you correctly so that they will be effective.

2. Employees whose noise exposure equals or exceeds 85 dBA over an eight-hour period are required to have an annual audiometric test to check their hearing.

3. Keep hearing protectors in good operational order with routine maintenance and replacement of defective parts.

4. Don't use homemade hearing protectors such as wadded cotton or tissue paper. They don't work.

5. Wear ear protection at home for any noisy job like operating a chainsaw or using various kinds of shop equipment. And watch the volume on your stereo headphones.

The sounds of everyday life — nature, music, the voices of family and friends — all add pleasure and meaning to our lives. Value them enough to protect your hearing.

Safe at Home

Hearing loss can result from exposure to any source of excessive noise, even if you aren't at work. For example, you can be exposed to high noise levels when you:

- Use power tools.

- Attend concerts and sporting events.

- Listen to loud music on head phones.

- Shoot targets at a gun range.

It's just as important to wear hearing protection during these noisy activities as it is to wear it in a noisy workplace.

Even if you aren't exposed to noise at work, consider having periodic hearing tests to identify any developing hearing loss.

Employee _____

Instructor _____

Date _____

Location _____

HEARING CONSERVATION REVIEW

1. The ear:
   a. Changes the energy in sound waves into nerve impulses.
   b. Naturally blocks unsafe noise levels.
   c. Changes nerve impulses into sound waves.
   d. Is damaged by any sound.

2. _____ is measured in decibels (dB):
   a. A sound wave.
   b. Loudness.
   c. Pitch.
   d. Frequency.

3. _____ is more damaging to your hearing:
   a. High-frequency sound.
   b. Low-frequency sound.
   c. A sudden nerve impulse.
   d. Intensity.

4. OSHA says hearing protection must be provided when workers may be exposed to:
   a. 85 dB or more averaged over an 8-hour period.
   b. 85 dB or more at any instant.
   c. More than 50 dB averaged over one shift.
   d. Any noise that isn't reduced by engineering controls.

5. Wide band noise:
   a. Is made up of a many impulses.
   b. Is produced before narrow band noise can occur.
   c. Is made up of a wide range of frequencies.
   d. Is mostly associated with the noise from a jack hammer or a punch press.

6. Narrow band noise:
   a. Is made up of wide band noise.
   b. Has low intensity.
   c. Is less than 85 dB.
   d. Is made up of a narrow range of frequencies.

7. Impulse noise:
   a. Is made up of high-frequency waves.
   b. Is made up of "beats" that repeat in a pattern.
   c. Must be more than 100 dB.
   d. Can't cause hearing loss.

8. Temporary hearing loss:
   a. Doesn't occur.
   b. Can occur from a short exposure to loud noise.
   c. Happens if you're exposed to loud noise for a long period of time.
   d. Can only happen if the exposure is from wide band noise.

9. Any hearing protector:
   a. Completely blocks out all sound.
   b. Offers complete protection from any hearing loss.
   c. Reduces the amount of sound reaching the delicate parts of the ear.
   d. Equally reduces the force of high frequency and low frequency noise.

10. Wearing both ear plugs and ear muffs gives you:
    a. The same protection as the ear plugs alone.
    b. The same protection as the ear muffs alone.
    c. About 3 to 5 dB more protection than either device alone.
    d. Twice the amount of protection.

LIFTING AND ERGONOMICS

Most heavy objects are usually lifted by forklifts, hoists, dollies, and other types of equipment. However, sometimes it is necessary to load or unload materials by hand.

In addition, jobs can expose workers to specialized tasks, higher assembly line speeds, and increased repetition that can be related to chronic or acute injury. Workers' hands, wrists, arms, shoulders, backs, and legs may be subjected to repetitive twisting, forceful, or flexing motions; excessive vibration; and awkward postures during a typical workday. Recognizing ergonomic hazards in the workplace is the first step in improving worker protection

Basics of Safe Lifting

To avoid injury, it is important to follow proper lifting procedures.

1. **Size up the load before trying to lift it**. Test the weight by moving one of the corners. If the load is too heavy or of an awkward shape, the best thing to do is:

   - Get help from a co-worker.

   - Use a mechanical lifting device.

   - Break down the load into smaller parts if you can.

2. **Make sure you can carry the load where you need to go before attempting to move it**. Also, make sure your path is clear of obstacles and that there are no hazards, such as spilled grease or oil in your path. Turn your body by changing foot positions, and have sure footing before setting out.

3. **Bend the knees**. This is the single most important rule when lifting moderate to heavy objects.

   • Position your feet close to the load.

   • Center yourself over the load.

   • Bend your knees and get a good hand hold.

   • Straighten your legs to lift straight up, smoothly.

   • Allow your legs, not your back, to do the work.

4. **Do not twist or turn your body once you have made the lift.** Keep the load close to your body, and keep it steady. Avoid any sudden twisting or turning.

5. **Set the load down properly**. Setting the load down is just as important as lifting it. Lower the load slowly by bending your knees, letting your legs do most of the work. Don't let go of the load until it is securely in place.

6. **Always push, not pull**, the object when possible. When moving an object on rollers, for example, pushing puts less strain on the back and is safer, should the object tip.

Planning Ahead

Planning ahead makes sense. If you know certain loads will have to be carried from storage, place the objects on racks, not on the floor, whenever possible. That way, the load will not have to be lifted from the floor. Do not attempt to carry loads that are clearly too heavy for you. Long objects, such as pipes and lumber, may not be heavy, but the weight might not be balanced. Such objects should be carried by two or more people.

If a heavy load can be split up into smaller ones, you're better off doing that, even if loading takes a few extra minutes. Trying to lift it all at once may be asking for trouble.

When catching falling or tossed objects, your feet should be firmly planted, with your back straight and your knees slightly bent. Your legs should absorb the impact, not your back. If you're working on something low, bend your knees. Keep your back as straight as possible. Bending from the waist can lead to back pain. In both of these situations, frequent rest breaks are necessary to keep from getting back fatigue.

What Are Back Injuries?

Sprains and strains are the most common types of back injury. Your back can be injured by improper lifting, falling, auto accidents, and sports activities. But of these, lifting improperly is a big cause of back pain and injury.

Problems with the lower back are a frequent cause of lost work time and workers' compensation.

Here are some things that can go wrong with the back:

- **Strains and sprains** can result from injury to muscles and ligaments that support the back. A torn ligament will result in severe back pain.

- **Ruptured or slipped disk** occurs when the disk (vertebral cushion) presses on a nerve.

- **Chronic tension or stress** can result in muscle spasms and aggravate persistent and painful backache.

- **Other conditions** such as pain "referred to the back" from other organs, such as the kidneys and prostate, can result in nagging back pain.

Why Back Pain Happens

Using improper lifting techniques can lead to back injuries, but other factors can contribute to this age-old problem.

Poor Posture

Whether you're standing, sitting, or reclining, posture affects the amount of strain put on your back. When standing correctly, the spine has a natural "S" curve. The shoulders are back and the "S" curve is directly over the pelvis.

Good sitting posture should put your knees slightly higher than your hips. Your hips should be to the rear of the chair with your lower back not overly arched. Also, your shoulders and upper back are not rounded. Reclining posture is important, too. Sleep on your side with knees bent, or sleep on your back. Sleeping on your stomach, especially on a sagging mattress with your head on a thick pillow, puts too much strain on the spine. Result: morning backache.

Poor Physical Condition

Your physical condition can lead to back pain. If you are overweight, and especially if you have developed a pot belly, extra strain on your spine results. An estimate is that every extra pound up front puts 10 pounds of strain on your back.

Infrequent exercise is a major factor for chronic back pain, too. A sudden strain on generally unused back muscles leads to trouble. Proper diet and exercise is the sensible way to help avoid back problems.

Repetitive Trauma

Many back injuries do not come from a single lift but occur from relatively minor strains over time.

Back injuries, as with other cumulative trauma disorders (CTDs), may arise from repeated injuries. As the worker repeats a particular irritating movement, the minor injuries begin to accumulate and weaken affected muscles or ligaments. Eventually a more serious injury may occur. Thus, a single overexertion may actually have little to do with an injury.

Remember to use mechanical lifting aids when appropriate, along with good lifting techniques, whenever you do any lifting.

Certain jobs require long hours of standing or sitting. Get up and stretch frequently if you are required to sit for long periods. If standing, ease the strain on your lower back by changing foot positions often, placing one foot on a rail or ledge. However, keep your weight evenly balanced when standing. Don't lean to one side.

What Is Ergonomics?

Ergonomics is a discipline that involves arranging the environment to fit the person. An example of good ergonomic design can be as simple as a well-designed hand tool or as elaborate as adjustable workstations on a production line.

Following ergonomic principles helps reduce stress and eliminate many potential injuries and disorders associated with overuse of muscles, bad posture, and repeated physical tasks. The objective of ergonomics is to reduce worker stress and injury through design of tasks, workstations, controls, displays, safety devices, tools, lighting, and equipment.

Where Are the Regulations?

The Occupational Safety and Health Administration's (OSHA)
Ergonomics Program standard was repealed before it took
effect in 2001. OSHA plans to continue to investigate
ergonomic hazards and can cite employers using Section
5(a)(1) (the General Duty Clause) of the OSH Act. Even
without a regulation, some employers are finding that taking
relatively simple steps can resolve ergonomic issues.

Disorders/Injuries Related to Ergonomic Hazards

A variety of musculoskeletal disorders are caused by
ergonomic stressors.

Cumulative Trauma Disorders

CTDs are disorders of the musculoskeletal and nervous
systems which are caused or made worse by repetitive
motions, forceful exertions, vibration, contact with hard and
sharp edges, or sustained or awkward postures.

CTDs can affect nearly all tissues, the nerves, tendons,
tendon sheaths, and muscles, with the upper extremities
being the most frequently affected. These injuries typically
develop gradually over time.

CTDs in the workplace are often tendon disorders, which
may occur at or near the joints where the tendons rub
against ligaments and bones. The most frequently noted
symptoms of tendon disorders are a dull aching sensation
over the tendon, discomfort with specific movements, and
tenderness to the touch. Recovery is usually slow, and the
condition may easily become chronic if the cause is not
eliminated. Tendon disorders can arise from a wide variety of
occupational motions and actions.

Carpal Tunnel Syndrome

Carpal Tunnel Syndrome (CTS) is a specific CTD affecting
the hands and wrists, and this condition has probably
received more attention in recent years than any other CTD.

The pressure of repetitive motion causes tingling, numbness, or severe pain in the wrist and hand. The pressure also results in a lack of strength in the hand and an inability to make a fist, hold objects, or perform other manual tasks. If the pressure continues, it can damage the nerve, causing permanent loss of sensation and even partial paralysis.

Employees are often unaware of the causes of CTS. Often they do not associate their pain with their work because symptoms may only occur during evening or off-duty hours.

Contributing Factors

Worker/workplace interactions which cause musculoskeletal disorders include heavy lifting, constant twisting, and repeated motions. In addition, physical characteristics of the worker, including size, endurance, range of motion, strength, gender, and other factors vary from  person to person. When the job demand exceeds the physical characteristics of the worker, an injury is likely to result.

One way your employer may uncover ergonomic hazards is by doing a worksite analysis. Possible risk factors for cumulative trauma and back disorders that may be identified with a worksite analysis include:

- Regular repetitive tasks.

- Awkward postures.

- Forceful exertions.

- Temperature extremes.

- Inappropriate hand tools.

- Restrictive workstations.

- Vibration from power tools.

- Poor body mechanics.

- Lifting heavy or awkward objects.

The combined effect of several risk factors often results in the onset of CTDs.

Hazard Prevention and Control

Ergonomic hazards are prevented primarily by the effective design of a job or jobsite and the tools or equipment used in that job. Based on information gathered in the worksite analysis, procedures can be established to correct or control ergonomic hazards using the following methods.

Engineering Controls

The primary focus of fixing ergonomic problems is to make the job fit the person, not force the person to fit the job. Engineering controls can accomplish this by ergonomically designing workstations, tools, and equipment.

Your workstation should accommodate the full range of movements you need to do your job. It should let you assume several different but equally healthful and safe postures that still let you do your job:

- You should have enough space for your knees and feet.

- You should be able to adjust the height of worktables and chairs so that you have proper back and leg support. (You can use seat cushions to compensate for height variation when chairs or stools are not adjustable.)

- You should be able to easily reach materials, tools, and machine controls.

Other factors the employer will look at include the need to exert force, contact with hard or sharp edges, proper seating, work piece orientation, and layout of the workstation.

Other engineering adaptations can be made to tools and tool handles.

Several factors should be considered when selecting a tool, including:

- Position in which it will be used.
- Vibration.
- Grip strength required.
- Awkwardness.
- Force required.
- Repetitive motion involved.
- Handle sizes and their adequacy for gloved hands.
- Accommodation of both right- and left-handed workers.
- Balance.
- Center of gravity.
- Weight of the tool.
- Whether or not the tool is appropriate for the job.

Administrative Controls

Administrative controls are used to reduce the duration, frequency, and severity of exposure to ergonomic stressors. Once ergonomic problems have been identified, your supervisor may opt to train you on ways to avoid injury at your job, reduce the number of repetitions you make, provide rest breaks, or begin cross-training so that you may rotate jobs with co-workers.

Work Practice Controls

Key elements of a good work practice program include instruction in proper work techniques, employee training and conditioning, regular monitoring, feedback, adjustments, modification, and maintenance.

For example, after you are trained in a particular work activity, such as proper lifting or proper tool handling, your supervisor should monitor you to make sure you continue to use the proper techniques. Improper practices should be corrected to prevent injury.

Work at Working Safely

With proper exercise, a good diet, and the proper lifting techniques, your chances of being out of work with chronic or severe back pain are greatly reduced. Remember to:

1. Be aware of proper posture.

2. Follow a sensible diet and exercise program.

3. Get help to lift objects that are too heavy for you.

4. Plan ahead when lifting jobs are necessary.

5. Lift with the legs, not your back.

6. Make sure your path is clear and be careful of your footing.

7. Never twist or turn suddenly while carrying a heavy load.

8. Bend your knees to lower the load as you set it down.

In addition, you need to be aware of ergonomics and the causes of musculoskeletal disorders and CTDs.

1. Cooperate with your employer in making ergonomically designed changes in the workplace.

2. Be aware of the signs and symptoms of CTDs, and see a doctor about any CTD-related injuries.

3. Become aware of job-specific techniques you can use to alleviate ergonomic problems.

Safe at Home

When you're at home, you might not do the same type of repetitive lifting as you do at work, but you're probably more likely to do manual lifting. Dollies, hoists, and other lifting aids usually aren't readily available around the house.

The same tips for doing manual lifting at work apply when you're off the clock:

- Size up the load before you lift it. Consider getting someone to help you, using an available lifting device, and breaking up loads into smaller parts.

168

- Clear your path and a space to set down the load.

- When you lift, get close to the load, bend your knees, and get a good grip. Straighten your legs to lift the load.

- Carry the load close to your body and avoid any sudden twisting or turning.

- Bend your knees to lower the load into place.

- If you're using a wheelbarrow or cart, push the load instead of pulling it.

NOTES

Employee _____

Instructor _____

Date _____

Location _____

LIFTING AND ERGONOMICS REVIEW

1. If a load is an awkward shape or too heavy for one person to lift:
   a. Use a mechanical lifting device.
   b. Break up the load into smaller parts.
   c. Get a helper.
   d. All of the above.

2. The next step after you size up a load before trying to lift it is to:
   a. Bend you back as you lift.
   b. Hold the load close to your body.
   c. Make sure you can carry to load where you need to go with it.
   d. None of the above.

3. When you carry a load, you should avoid:
   a. Sudden twisting or turning.
   b. Holding the load close to your body.
   c. Changing your foot positions to change directions.
   d. Taking a clear path.

4. Part of safe lifting is to bend your knees:
   a. Only when you pick up the load.
   b. Only when you set down a load.
   c. When you pick up and set down the load.
   d. When you change directions.

5. Storing materials on racks and shelves:
   a. Isn't a good practice.
   b. Will keep you from having to bend to lift them from floor level.
   c. Is the best way to keep them clean.
   d. Is an OSHA requirement.

6. It's a good idea for two people to carry long objects:
    a. Because they're always too heavy.
    b. Because the weight might not be evenly balanced.
    c. So you can get around corners.
    d. So you have a spotter when you set it down.

7. Cumulative trauma disorders:
    a. Happen suddenly from a single overexertion.
    b. Result directly from poor diet and a lack of exercise.
    c. Result from sitting or standing.
    d. Happen from repeated minor injuries.

8. The discipline that involves arranging the environment to fit the person is called:
    a. Work practice controls.
    b. Conditioning.
    c. Ergonomics.
    d. None of the above.

9. Ergonomics helps reduce or eliminate disorders associated with:
    a. Bad posture.
    b. Overuse of muscles.
    c. Repeated physical tasks.
    d. All of the above.

10. An example of an ergonomic engineering control is:
    a. Cross-training so workers can rotate jobs.
    b. Using adjustable-height chairs and tables.
    c. Monitoring how employees follow lifting procedures.
    d. Providing rest breaks.

LOCKOUT/TAGOUT

Lockout/tagout procedures are designed to prevent accidents and injuries caused by the unexpected release of energy when equipment is being repaired or maintained.

Where Are the Regulations?

The Occupational Safety and Health Administration (OSHA) regulates lockout/tagout through the Control of Hazardous Energy standard, found at 29 CFR 1910.147. This standard mandates training, audits, and recordkeeping to ensure that workers will not be injured by unintentionally energized equipment.

What Is Lockout/Tagout?

Lockout is the process of preventing the flow of energy from a power source to a piece of equipment, and keeping it from operating.

Lockout is accomplished by installing a lockout device at the power source so that equipment powered by that source cannot be operated. A lockout device is a lock, block, or chain that keeps a switch, valve, or lever in the off position.

Locks are provided by the employer and can be used only for lockout purposes. They should never be used to lock tool boxes, storage sheds, or other items.

Tagout is accomplished by placing a tag on the power source. The tag acts as a warning not to restore energy — it is not a physical restraint. Tags must clearly state: **Do not operate** or the like, and must be applied by hand.

Both locks and tags must be strong enough to prevent unauthorized removal and to withstand various environmental conditions.

What Must Be Locked or Tagged Out

The lockout/tagout standard covers servicing and maintenance of equipment where unexpected energization or start-up of equipment could harm employees.

In general, OSHA requires that all power sources that *can* be locked out, must be *locked out* for servicing or maintenance. Guards or interlock devices cannot be used as substitutes for locks.

Power Sources That Cannot Be Locked Out

In very rare cases, a power source cannot be physically locked out. Discuss this situation with your supervisor to find out if *tagout alone* may safely be used. There are a few situations where tagout alone is allowed.

Follow the Plan

The standard requires that employers develop written energy control programs that clearly and specifically explain all procedures for lockout/tagout. These plans must include:

- Lockout/tagout procedures.
- Employee training.
- Periodic inspections.

Employers must identify and differentiate between authorized and affected employees. **Authorized employees** physically lock or tag out equipment for servicing or maintenance. Note that these individuals are not necessarily the people who normally operate the equipment.

Affected employees are those workers whose job requires them to operate equipment subject to lockout/tagout, or those employees who work in areas where lockout/tagout is used. Affected employees stay clear of equipment while it is locked out.

Controlling Energy Sources

A wide variety of energy sources require lockout/ tagout to protect you from the release of hazardous energy. Some of these energy sources include:

- **Electrical**

- **Mechanical**

- **Pneumatic** (involving gases, especially air)

- **Hydraulic** (involving fluids)

- **Chemical**

- **Thermal**

- **Water under pressure** (or steam)

- **Gravity**

- **Potential**

Some of the problems of hazardous energy include:

- **Accidental start-ups**

- **Electric shock**

- **Release of stored, residual, or potential energy**

The Lockout/Tagout Procedure

Lockout/tagout procedures cover the following:

- The scope and purpose of lockout/tagout.

- How to perform a shutdown, including isolating, blocking, and securing machines or equipment.

- How to place, remove, and transfer locks and who is responsible for them.

- How to test the machine to make sure it is locked out.

Preparing for a Shutdown

Before authorized employees ever turn off a machine as part of a lockout/tagout procedure, they must know:

- The type and magnitude of the energy involved.

- Associated hazards of the energy involved.

- Control methods for the energy involved.

Performing a Shutdown

First, authorized employees notify all affected employees that they are about to start a lockout procedure. Then they locate all energy sources that power the piece of equipment. Some machines may have more than one source of power. Follow the procedures to shut down each machine.

Isolating Equipment and Applying Lockout Devices

Machines or equipment to be locked out should already be capable of being locked out. Every power source has its own procedure for lockout. Lockout may be accomplished by pulling a plug, opening a disconnect switch, closing a valve, bleeding a line, or placing a block in the equipment. Generally, authorized employees follow this sequence of events:

- After they have completed the shutdown, they turn off the energy at the main power source.

- Using their designated locks, they lock out all energy sources involved.

- They attempt to restart the machine to guarantee that the power is shut off, then they return the control knob to the off position.

If several people are needed to work on a piece of equipment, each one must apply his or her own locks. This prevents any accidental start-ups while another employee may still be working on the machinery. In this case, they'll use a **multiple lockout device** that can accommodate several locks at once.

Note: Authorized employees may never use another employee's lock and may never lend theirs.

Safe Release of Stored Energy

Equipment must be at "zero energy state" before servicing or maintenance work can begin. To get to this zero energy state, authorized employees:

- Drain all valves, bleed off air from a system, eliminate stored hydraulic pressure, or use any method to release energy that is detailed in the lockout/tagout procedure.

- Test the machine to make sure that all energy was disconnected or released.

Verify That the Machine Is Locked Out

Before authorized employees start to repair or service the machine, they make sure that it has been properly isolated and deenergized. With locks in place, they try to start the machine to make sure it can't be turned on.

Restoring Power

After servicing is finished, authorized employees check that all tools are removed from the area and replace all machine guards. They make sure all employees are clear of the machine. Only then can they remove the locks and reconnect all sources of energy. After this, they are to notify the affected employees that the lockout has been removed and the machine can be restarted.

Training and Audit Requirements

OSHA requires that:

- All **authorized employees** be trained in the recognition of applicable hazardous energy sources, the type and magnitude of hazardous energy sources in use at the facility, and how to perform the lockout/tagout procedures.

- All **affected employees** must be trained in the purpose and use of lockout/tagout.

- All other employees must be instructed on the purpose of the plan, but not in its actual use.

- Periodic inspections or audits must be performed by an authorized employee who does not use the energy control procedure being inspected.

- Retraining must be done when there are changes in equipment, job assignment, or procedures, when an audit shows deficiencies with the procedure, and when the employer feels the procedures should be reviewed.

Audits must be done at least annually, and should include questions to determine if employees understand the purpose of lockout/tagout, if proper locks and tags are being used, and if established procedures are being followed. Each audit must be documented.

Other Concerns

Other concerns that must be addressed for your organization's lockout/tagout program include working with outside contractors and shift and personnel changes.

Outside Contractors

Outside contractors must be informed of your lockout/tagout procedure in full detail so that their employees understand the meaning of locks or tags that they may come across during the course of their work. In addition, if contractors will be using locks or tags, they should inform your employer so that everyone affected may be notified.

Shift and Personnel Changes

In general, if a piece of equipment is locked out at shift change, the person on the next shift must apply his lock before the employee who is leaving can remove his.

Work at Working Safely

Always follow lockout/tagout procedures during servicing or maintenance of equipment where unexpected energization or start-up of the equipment could harm you or a fellow employee.

1. Always lock and tag out power sources and switches when you service or repair energized equipment.

2. Never ignore or remove the locks or tags of other employees when you come across them in the workplace.

3. Know your role as an authorized or affected employee.

NOTES

Employee _____

Instructor _____

Date _____

Location _____

LOCKOUT/TAGOUT REVIEW

1. Lockout/tagout requirements apply:
   a. When equipment is being repaired or maintained.
   b. When equipment is being used in normal production.
   c. When access to an area is restricted.
   d. When turning off equipment at the end of a shift.

2. Lockout keeps equipment from operating:
   a. By posting a sign in the area.
   b. Through the use of barrier tape.
   c. By installing a lockout device at the power source.
   d. By assigning someone to keep people away.

3. Lockout locks can also be used for:
   a. Locking tool boxes.
   b. Locking storage sheds.
   c. Locking doors to restricted areas.
   d. None of the above.

4. A tagout tag:
   a. Warns people to not restore energy to the equipment.
   b. Must be applied by hand.
   c. Must state "Do not operate" or something similar.
   d. All of the above.

5. If a power source can't be locked out:
   a. The equipment can't be repaired.
   b. The equipment must be repaired when no employees are at work.
   c. The authorized employee may be able to use tagout alone.
   d. The equipment must be changed so it accepts a lock.

6. Authorized employees:
   a. Are always the people who normally operate the equipment.
   b. Physically lock or tag out the equipment.
   c. Ask their supervisors to apply the lockout locks.
   d. Can remove any other authorized employee's lockout device.

7. Affected employees:
   a. Operate equipment that may be locked out.
   b. Work in areas where lockout/tagout is used.
   c. Stay clear of equipment while it's locked out.
   d. All of the above.

8. After equipment is shut down, the authorized employee:
   a. Turns off the energy at the main power source.
   b. Finds out the hazards associated with the equipment's energy supply.
   c. Asks an affected employee to apply lockout locks.
   d. All of the above.

9. Authorized employees try to start the machine while the locks are in place:
   a. Never.
   b. To verify that the machine is locked out.
   c. To test or position the equipment during the repair.
   d. Only if more than one person will be doing repairs at the same time.

10. If an authorized person on the next shift will continue the repair:
    a. He must apply his own lock.
    b. The authorized employee on the first shift must leave his lock in place.
    c. A new lockout permit must be signed.
    d. He can work without the protection of a lock.

MACHINE GUARDING

While machines allow more efficient, productive work, you must use them with great caution. It's up to you to make sure all machine guards are in place, wear protective equipment, and use safety features and tools correctly.

Where Are the Regulations?

The Occupational Safety and Health Administration (OSHA) has issued several regulations that apply to the use of powered machinery, under Subpart O, Machinery and Machine Guarding, and Subpart P, Hand and Portable-Powered Tools and other Hand-Held Equipment. These rules can be found in 29 CFR 1910.211-.244.

There are also guarding requirements under resistance welding at 29 CFR 1910.255(a)(4) and (b)(4). These requirements touch on lockout/tagout procedures during welding operations and point of operation guards for press welding machines.

In general, remember that any machine part, function, or process which may cause injury must be guarded. Where the operation of a machine, or accidental contact with it, can injure you or others, the hazard must be either controlled or eliminated.

Serious Injuries Are Possible

Crushed hands and arms, severed fingers, blindness — the list of possible machinery-related injuries is as long as it is horrifying. Guards are essential for protecting workers from needless and preventable injuries.

Where Mechanical Hazards Occur

These types of dangerous moving parts need guarding:

- **The point of operation**, or that point where work is performed on the material, such as cutting, shaping, boring, or forming of stock.

- **Power transmission apparatus**, or the components of the mechanical system which transmit energy to the part of the machine performing the work. These components include flywheels, pulleys, belts, connecting rods, couplings, cams, spindles, chains, cranks, and gears.

- **Other moving parts**, or parts of the machine which move while the machine is working, can include reciprocating, rotating, and transverse moving parts, as well as feed mechanisms and auxiliary parts of the machine.

Hazardous Mechanical Motions and Actions

Different types of hazardous mechanical motions and actions are basic to nearly all machines. All motions can cause serious injuries.

Rotating motion can be dangerous; even smooth, slowly rotating shafts can grip clothing, and skin contact can force an arm or hand into a dangerous position. Injuries due to contact with rotating parts can be severe.

Collars, couplings, cams, clutches, flywheels, shaft ends, spindles, and horizontal or vertical shafting are some examples of common rotating mechanisms which may be hazardous. There is added danger when bolts, nicks, abrasions, and projecting keys or set screws are exposed on rotating parts on machinery.

In-running nip points, or those locations that can capture body parts in rotating machinery parts, are common. There are three main types of nip points:

- Parts that rotate in opposite directions while their axes are parallel to each other. These parts may be in contact or in close proximity to each other. This danger is common on machinery with intermeshing gears, rolling mills, and calenders.

- Another type of nip point is created between rotating and tangentially moving parts. Some examples would be the point of contact between a power transmission belt and its pulley, a chain and sprocket, or a rack and pinion.

- Nip points can also occur between rotating and fixed parts which create a shearing, crushing, or abrading action, for example, spoked handwheels or flywheels.

Reciprocating motions may be hazardous because, during the back-and-forth or up-and-down motion, you might get struck by or caught between a moving and stationary part.

Transverse motion (movement in a straight, continuous line) creates a hazard because a worker may be struck or caught in a pinch or shear point by a moving part.

Cutting action hazards exist at the point of operation in cutting wood, metal, or other materials. Typical machines having cutting hazards include bandsaws, circular saws, boring or drilling machines, turning machines (lathes), or milling machines. Flying chips or scrap material can also strike the eyes or face.

Punching action results when power is applied to a slide (ram) for blanking, drawing, or stamping metal or other materials. The danger of this type of action occurs at the point of operation where stock is inserted, held, and withdrawn by hand. Typical machinery used for punching operations are power presses and iron workers.

Shearing action involves applying power to a slide or knife in order to trim or shear metal or other materials. A hazard occurs at the point of operation where stock is actually inserted, held, and withdrawn. Machinery used for shearing operations includes mechanically, hydraulically, or pneumatically powered shears.

Bending action results when power is applied to a slide in order to draw or stamp metal or other materials. A hazard occurs at the point of operation where stock is inserted, held, and withdrawn. Power presses, press brakes, and tubing benders all use bending action.

Guard Requirements

What must a guard do to protect you from mechanical hazards? Guards must meet these minimum general requirements:

- **Prevent contact**: The guard must prevent hands, arms, or any part of your body or clothing from making contact with dangerous moving parts.

- **Secure**: Guards should not be easy to remove or alter. Guards should be made of durable material and be firmly secured to the machine.

- **Protect from falling objects**: The guard should ensure that no objects can fall into moving parts.

- **Create no new hazards**: A guard defeats its own purpose if it creates a hazard of its own such as shear point or a jagged edge.

- **Create no interference**: The guard should not keep you from doing your job. If possible, maintenance workers should be able to lubricate the machine without removing the guards.

Machine Guarding Methods

Safeguards can be grouped under five general categories:

Guards are physical barriers which prevent access to danger areas.

A safety **device** may perform one of several functions. It may:

- Stop the machine if a hand or any part of the body is inadvertently placed in the danger area.

- Restrain or withdraw the operator's hands from the danger area during operation.

- Require the operator to use both hands on machine controls, thus keeping both hands and body out of danger.

- Provide a barrier which is synchronized with the operating cycle of the machine in order to prevent entry to the danger area during the hazardous part of the cycle.

Guarding by location or distance has many applications. To guard a machine by location, the machine or its dangerous moving parts must be positioned so that hazardous areas are not accessible or do not present a hazard during the normal machine operation. For example, locating a machine so that a wall protects the worker is guarding by location.

Feeding and ejection methods of guarding limit hazards associated with feeding stock into a machine.

Miscellaneous aids provide an extra margin of safety. One example is an awareness barrier that serves to remind you that you are approaching a danger area.

Personal Protective Equipment

Engineering controls that eliminate the hazard at the source and do not rely on behavior for their effectiveness offer the best and most reliable means of safeguarding. Therefore, engineering controls must be the employer's first choice for eliminating machine hazards. But whenever engineering controls are not available or are not fully capable of protecting you, you must wear protective clothing or personal protective equipment (PPE).

For example, caps and hair nets can help keep your hair from being caught in machinery.

It is important to note that protective clothing and equipment can create hazards. A protective glove can become caught between rotating parts, or a respirator facepiece can hinder the wearer's vision, for example.

Other clothing may present additional safety hazards. For example, loose-fitting shirts might possibly become entangled in rotating spindles or other kinds of moving machinery. Jewelry, such as chains, watches, and rings, can catch on machine parts or stock and lead to serious injury by pulling a hand, or head, into the danger area.

Grounding Is an Important Precaution

Most machines and power tools are powered by electricity. Electricity will give you a shock if you accidentally become part of the electrical path to ground.

Grounding electrical current is one of the most important safety measures to take when working with electric equipment. Grounding provides a safe path for electricity, preventing leakage of current in circuits and equipment. Grounding should be provided for the entire system and individual pieces of equipment. Check all ground connections regularly for tightness.

Work at Working Safely

You should be aware of the following:

1. The hazards associated with particular machines.

2. How guards provide protection.

3. How and why to use the guards.

4. How and under what circumstances guards can be removed, and by whom (in most cases, repair or maintenance personnel only).

5. What to do (e.g. contact your supervisor) if a guard is damaged, missing, or unable to provide adequate protection.

NOTES

Employee _____

Instructor _____

Date _____

Location _____

MACHINE GUARDING REVIEW

1. In general, any machine part that may cause injury:
   a. Must always be locked out.
   b. Must be guarded.
   c. Must be painted blue.
   d. Must have a warning sticker on it.

2. Flywheels, pulleys, belts, chains, gears, etc. are components of the:
   a. Point of operation.
   b. Power transmission apparatus.
   c. Feed mechanism.
   d. Auxiliary machine parts.

3. Shaft ends, spindles, collars, and couplings are examples of common:
   a. Rotating machine parts.
   b. Reciprocating machine parts.
   c. Shear points.
   d. None of the above.

4. What can capture body parts in rotating machinery parts?
   a. Bending action.
   b. Nip points.
   c. Fixed barrier guards.
   d. Transverse motion.

5. General requirements for machine guards include:
   a. Preventing contact and being secured to the machine.
   b. Ensuring that no objects can fall into moving parts.
   c. Creating no new hazards and not interfering with machine operation.
   d. All of the above.

6. General categories for safeguards include:
   a. Safety devices such as two-handed trip controls.
   b. Guarding by location.
   c. Guards that are physical barriers that prevent access.
   d. All of the above.

7. A safeguard that automatically stops the machine if part of the body enters the danger area is a:
   a. Fixed barrier guard.
   b. Miscellaneous aid.
   c. Safety device.
   d. Two-handed trip control.

8. Positioning dangerous moving parts where no one can access them is an example of:
   a. An OSHA violation.
   b. Guarding by location.
   c. A nip point.
   d. A synchronized barrier.

9. Protective clothing and personal protective equipment:
   a. Is needed if engineered machine safeguards don't provide complete protection.
   b. Is more hazardous than a loose-fitting shirt.
   c. Is the first choice for eliminating machine hazards.
   d. All of the above.

10. If the operation of a machine, or accidental contact with it can cause injury:
    a. The hazard must be controlled or eliminated.
    b. The machine must be locked out.
    c. The machine must be operated by remote control.
    d. None of the above.

MATERIALS HANDLING EQUIPMENT

Often, a load is too heavy to move manually, and it might not be safe or feasible to handle the load with a forklift. In these situations, a hoist or crane can be used to safely lift the load.

Where Are the Regulations?

The Occupational Safety and Health Administration (OSHA) has developed rules governing materials handling. These rules are found at 29 CFR 1910.176 through .184 in Subpart N. Your employer must train you to operate materials handling equipment safely. When hoist and crane safety is involved, strict inspection, maintenance, and operating procedures must be followed.

What Are the Hazards?

Some of the equipment that OSHA's rules apply to includes:

- Slings.

- Overhead and gantry cranes.

- Derricks.

If materials handling equipment is defective and fails during use, a heavy load could shift and fall. A load can also shift and fall if it is not properly rigged for lifting.

As loads are moved, the equipment operator must make sure that the load and the equipment have plenty of room to clear obstacles. If the load or equipment suddenly hits an object in the path, the load could shift and fall.

Electrical hazards need to be avoided during materials handling operations, too. The load and equipment needs to maintain a safe clearance near overhead electrical lines. If proper clearance is not maintained, the load or equipment can become energized and cause electrocutions.

Know Your Place Around Equipment

OSHA requires that only designated personnel be permitted to operate a crane or derrick. Whenever a crane or derrick is in operation, the operator must stay at the controls. And, only designated personnel can perform equipment repairs.

If you are not a designated operator, you should stay clear of the area where loads are being moved. Never stand under a raised load. If you hear a warning signal for an overhead or gantry crane operation, move to a safe area. Of course, never attempt to ride a load.

If your job requires you to manually guide loads into place, use tag lines — never handle loaded slings or other rigging directly because a shifting load can easily crush a hand.

Follow Safe Inspection Procedures

Slings used with hoists or cranes need to be inspected for damage or defects every day before use. Alloy steel chain slings need a more thorough inspection at least annually. Slings that are damaged or defective must be immediately removed from service.

Cranes and derricks are complex equipment, and they need detailed inspections. OSHA requires both frequent (daily to monthly) and periodic (monthly to annually) inspections of this equipment.

Frequent inspections can include inspections of:

- Operating mechanisms (steering, lifting mechanisms, brakes, etc.).

- Hydraulic or air lines.

- Hooks.

- Ropes and chains.

- Electrical apparatus.

In addition, certified records must be kept for monthly inspections of hooks, chains, and ropes.

Periodic inspections include inspections of the same components, but the periodic inspection is more complete. Periodic inspections can include inspections of:

- Structural members of the equipment.

- Bolts and rivets.

- Sheaves and drums.

- Bearings, pins, shafts, gears, etc.

- Load, wind, and other operating indicators.

- Gasoline, diesel, or electrical systems.

- Chain drives and chains.

- Electrical components (controls, limit switches, push buttons, etc.).

- Travel, steering, locking devices, and tires.

- Brakes.

- Foundation or supports.

After any inspection, deficiencies must be carefully examined to determine if there is a safety hazard. Unsafe equipment may not be used.

Good Maintenance Is Important

Slings that are damaged or defective may only be repaired by a sling manufacturer or equivalent repair service.

Keeping a crane or derrick in good operating condition requires preventive maintenance as well as timely repairs. Designated maintenance personnel will follow the company's preventive maintenance program. The basis for this program is the manufacturer's recommendations on preventive maintenance.

Maintenance procedures must include the following precautions:

- Move the equipment to a location where it will cause the least amount of interference with other equipment or operations.

- Turn all controls to the "off" position.

- Lock the main or emergency switch in the "off" position.

- Place "Out of Order" signs on the equipment and on the hook or on the floor beneath the equipment.

- Provide rail stops or other suitable means to prevent the interference of other cranes operating on the same runway as the idle crane.

Do not operate the equipment after repairs or adjustments until all guards have been reinstalled, safety devices reactivated, and maintenance equipment removed.

Some components must be regularly adjusted to maintain their proper operation:

- Limit switches.
- Control switches.
- Brakes.
- Power plants

Plan the Lift

Every time a load is lifted, operators should make a final check of the equipment for additions and modifications, including:

- Checking tags, instruction plates, and decals that will indicate modifications.
- Making sure the equipment's safety factor has not been reduced by additions or modifications.

Operators must understand the characteristics of the load, including:

- Hazardous or toxic materials.
- Weight.
- Dimensions.
- Center of gravity.

In order to lift the load, safe rigging is extremely important. Hoist chains and ropes must be free of kinks and twists and may not be wrapped around a load. Slings or other appropriate devices must be used to support the load and attach it to the hook. Operators need to review rigging sketches and information, including:

- Lift points.

- Methods of attachment.

- Sling angles.

- Load vectors.

- Boom and swing angles.

- Crane orientations.

- Rated capacities.

- Other factors affecting equipment operation.

Since the characteristics of the load and lifting environment can change with each lift, operators need to review the operating procedures, including:

- Step-by-step procedures.

- Applicable rigging precautions.

- Safety measures.

- Emergency procedures.

Before operating a truck crane at an outdoor worksite, review the area and operation for possible hazards. The review should include possible interferences to a safe lift, including:

- Overhead lines.

- Unstable soil.

- High wind conditions.

- Other work activities in the area.

Maintain Proper Clearance

Where mechanical handling equipment is used, sufficient safe clearances must be allowed for aisles, at loading docks, through doorways, and wherever turns or passage must be made. The employer must post signs to warn of clearance limits.

Overhead and gantry cranes have some additional clearance requirements for the crane and the cab.

Derricks and crawler locomotive and truck cranes have special requirements for clearance from overhead electrical lines. If work is being done near energized overhead lines, the equipment must keep a clearance distance of ten feet if parts may be elevated near the lines. If the line's voltage is higher than 50 kilovolts (kV), the clearance distance is increased by four inches for each 10 kV increase. When a crane or derrick is in transit with its boom lowered, the clearance may be reduced to four feet (with a four inch increase for each 10 kV over 50 kV).

Know the Safe Operating Procedures

Some general safe operating procedures that apply to all types of cranes and derricks include:

- The load-rating must be posted or marked.

- Do not exceed load ratings.

- The load must be secured and balanced using a sling or other appropriate device.

- Hoist lines may not be kinked or twisted.

- The hook must not swing when it is brought over the load.

- There must be no sudden acceleration or deceleration of the load.

- The equipment may not be used to drag a load horizontally.

- Loads may not be raised over people, and people are not allowed to ride loads.

- Operators must test the brakes when lifting near-capacity loads.

- The operator's necessary clothing and personal belongings must be stored so they do not interfere with the equipment's access or operation.

- Tools, fuses, and oil cans are to be stored in a toolbox; they are not to lie loose in the cab.

- The operators must be familiar with the operation of the fire extinguishers provided with the equipment.

Work at Working Safely

When equipment is used to lift and carry heavy loads, it pays to take your time to be sure every step of the job is done correctly.

1. Stay clear of loads.

2. Take inspections seriously — find defects before they cause equipment to fail.

3. Promptly report problems with the equipment.

4. Take defective or damaged equipment out of service.

5. Plan the lift.

6. Rig the load safely.

7. Follow all manufacturers' operating instructions.

8. Maintain safe clearances.

Employee _____

Instructor _____

Date _____

Location _____

MATERIALS HANDLING EQUIPMENT REVIEW

1. A load could fall from material handling equipment:
   a. If a defect causes the equipment to fail during use.
   b. If the load isn't properly rigged.
   c. If the load or the equipment suddenly hits an obstacle.
   d. All of the above.

2. Who is responsible for making sure the load and the equipment stay clear of obstacles?
   a. Any employee working in the area.
   b. The crew chief.
   c. The person who is operating the material handling equipment.
   d. The safety manager.

3. Who can operate a crane or derrick?
   a. Only designated personnel.
   b. Any employee who needs something moved by the equipment.
   c. Any truck driver who needs to load his truck.
   d. Only the safety manager.

4. If you aren't operating an overhead or gantry crane:
   a. Move closer to the equipment if you hear a warning signal.
   b. Stand under the raised load.
   c. You may ride on stable loads for short distances.
   d. Stay clear of the area where loads are being moved.

5. Frequent inspections of cranes and derricks are required to be done:
   a. Annually.
   b. Every third Tuesday.
   c. Daily to monthly.
   d. Monthly to annually.

6. Certified records must be kept:
   a. For every daily inspection.
   b. For monthly inspections of hooks, chains, and ropes.
   c. For monthly inspections of bolts and rivets.
   d. For weekly tire inspections.

7. If any inspection finds a deficiency that's a safety hazard:
   a. The equipment may be used if a repair has been scheduled.
   b. The equipment's load rating drops by 50 percent.
   c. Only a designated mechanic can operate the equipment.
   d. The equipment may not be used.

8. To plan the lift, the equipment operator must understand the characteristics of the load, including:
   a. The rope's rated capacity.
   b. Decals that indicate modifications.
   c. The center of gravity.
   d. The limit switches.

9. When lifting loads near energized overhead lines, the equipment must keep a clearance distance of at least:
   a. Four feet if the boom is raised.
   b. 10 feet if the boom is lowered and the equipment is in transit.
   c. 10 feet, with an increase in the distance if the line is over 50 kilovolts.
   d. Eight feet if the load is less than five tons.

10. What must the operators test when lifting near-capacity loads?
    a. The fire extinguishers.
    b. The brakes.
    c. The soil conditions.
    d. The safety data sheet for the load.

RESPIRATORY PROTECTION

When ventilation or other engineering controls are not adequate to keep the air safe, a respirator will protect you.

Where Are the Regulations?

The Occupational Safety and Health Administration (OSHA) regulates the use of respirators in general industry, construction, and other industries. The regulation is at 29 CFR 1910.134.

Respiratory Protection Program

When respirators are required, your employer must have a worksite-specific respiratory protection program. The program includes:

- Procedures for selecting respirators.

- Medical evaluations.

- Fit testing for tight-fitting respirators.

- Procedures for proper use of respirators.

- Schedules and procedures for cleaning, disinfecting, storing, inspecting, repairing, discarding, and otherwise maintaining respirators.

- Procedures on safe air quality for atmosphere-supplying respirators.

- Training in respiratory hazards.

- Training in respirator use, maintenance, and the limitations of respirators.

- Procedures to make sure the program is effective.

If your employer allows you to wear a respirator on a volunteer basis (when the contaminants are at safe levels), the program only includes provisions for medical evaluations, cleaning, storage, and maintenance. (No program is needed if only disposable dust masks are used on a volunteer basis.)

Who Needs to Wear a Respirator?

You can't always see, smell, or taste the dust, smoke, mist, fumes, sprays, vapors, or gases that can be hazardous to your health. Your employer is responsible for determining when respirators are needed in the workplace.

What Types of Respirators Are Available?

There are two respirator types: air-purifying and atmosphere-supplying.

Air-Purifying

These respirators remove the contaminants from the air as you breathe. There must be enough oxygen in the air when using an air-purifying respirator. Typically, the respirator has a tight-fitting facepiece. As you inhale, a "negative pressure" suction inside of the facepiece forces the outside air through the respirator's cleaning elements before you breathe it. You must use a filter, cartridge, or canister that is approved for  the dust, mist, fume, aerosol, chemical vapor, or gas that you are exposed to.

Air-purifying respirators have limits on how long they will protect you. Filter media and sorbents get clogged or saturated as they are used. Follow your facility's cartridge or filter change schedule. The filters or cartridges can be used up before you notice a smell or taste inside of the respirator.

Warning: Not all types of hazardous substances can be safely removed by air-purifying respirators. In these cases, you'll need an atmosphere-supplying respirator.

Atmosphere-Supplying

Atmosphere-supplying respirators provide you with breathing air from a clean source. Supplied-Air Respirators (SARs) use an airline to feed clean air to the respirator's facepiece, helmet, or hood. A Self-Contained Breathing Apparatus (SCBA) supplies air from tanks that are carried by the user. Fire fighters typically wear SCBAs.

Atmosphere-supplying respirators blow air into a facepiece, helmet, or hood to create a "positive pressure" that prevents the hazardous air from leaking in. Frequently, these respirators are operated in the "pressure-demand" mode — this means that the air is regulated so more air is supplied as the wearer inhales.

People wearing SARs are limited in how much they can move around because of the airline. SCBAs are portable, but the tanks have limited operating times. Careful attention must be paid to the quality of the breathing air being supplied to the wearer of any atmosphere-supplying respirator.

Are You Physically Able to Wear a Respirator?

Wearing a respirator adds a physical burden to the job. Before you can be fit tested or required to wear a respirator, you must be evaluated by a physician or other licensed health care professional (PLHCP). You will need to fill out a medical questionnaire. You might need an exam and medical tests. The PLHCP will give you and your employer a written statement on your fitness to use the respirator. The PLHCP can limit how you use a respirator and can require periodic follow-up medical evaluations.

Selecting a Respirator

Your employer has to match the capabilities and limitations of the respirator to the hazards of the job. All respirators must be certified by the National Institute for Occupational Safety and Health (NIOSH) and must be used as they were intended to be used.

IDLH Atmospheres

If the respirator is to be used in an Immediately Dangerous to Life or Health (IDLH) atmosphere, it must be either:

- A full facepiece pressure demand SCBA certified by NIOSH for a minimum service life of thirty minutes, or

- A combination full facepiece pressure demand supplied-air respirator (SAR) with auxiliary self-contained air supply.

Non-IDLH Atmospheres

If the respirator is to be used in non-IDLH atmospheres (where there is enough oxygen and where contaminant levels are known) the respirator must be capable of protecting you from the contaminant levels that are expected during the job and in reasonably foreseeable emergency situations. Atmosphere-supplying respirators are appropriate for non-IDLH atmospheres.

For protection against gases and vapors, the employer can provide an air-purifying respirator in some non-IDLH situations. The canisters and cartridges must be approved for the hazards.

Air-purifying respirators can also be used to protect against particulates. NIOSH approval codes are based upon the filtering efficiency level and the filter's effectiveness on oil-based particulates.

How to Fit a Respirator

Before you can be required to use a respirator with a tight-fitting facepiece, you must pass a fit test. You cannot be fit tested if you have any facial hair growth (stubble beard growth, beard, mustache, or sideburns) between the facepiece sealing surface and your skin. You must have the fit re-tested at least annually. OSHA's procedures for conducting the fit test must be followed. The type of test depends on the type of respirator you are using. During the fit test, you will perform exercises while wearing the respirator, and a chemical test agent will be used to determine if the respirator is effective.

Using Your Respirator

Whenever you are wearing a respirator, make sure that you always leave the respirator use area:

- If you detect vapor or gas breakthrough, changes in breathing resistance, or facepiece leakage.

- If you need to change filter, cartridge, or canister elements.

- If you need to wash your face or the facepiece to prevent eye or skin irritation.

- If your respirator needs repairs.

Seal Checks

A good fit is important each time you wear a respirator with a tight-fitting facepiece. To make sure that your respirator has a good seal, you must perform two seal checks each time that you put on your respirator. General instructions for these checks are:

- **Positive pressure check** — Close off the exhalation valve and exhale gently into the facepiece. The seal is good if you feel a slight positive pressure built up inside the facepiece without air leaking out around the seal.

- **Negative pressure check** — Close off the inlet opening of the canister or cartridges by covering with your palm(s) or by replacing the filter seals. Inhale gently so that the facepiece collapses slightly, and hold your breath for ten seconds. The seal is good if the facepiece remains slightly collapsed and there is no air leaking in around the seal.

Prepare for Emergencies

If employees will be entering areas with IDLH atmospheres, at least one employee who is trained and equipped to provide rescue must remain outside and maintain communication with the employee(s) in the IDLH area. In addition, during interior structural firefighting, at least two employees equipped with SCBAs must enter the IDLH atmosphere together, and they must stay in contact with each other. Also, at least two people trained and equipped for rescue must remain outside during firefighting.

Know what to do in an emergency situation. If your respirator malfunctions while you are in a hazardous atmosphere, leave immediately. If your respirator is equipped with an auxiliary self-contained air supply, use it as you exit to safety.

Care and Maintenance of Respirators

Put a priority on keeping your respirator clean and in good repair. Don't risk irritations, disease, or contamination from using a dirty or damaged respirator.

If you have been issued your own respirator, clean and disinfect it as often as necessary to keep it clean. If a respirator is shared, clean it before the next person uses it. If a respirator is kept for emergency use only, clean it after each use. When you're done with fit testing or training exercises, clean those respirators, too.

Store your respirator so it is protected from damage, contamination, dust, sunlight, extreme temperatures, excessive moisture, and damaging chemicals. Facepieces and other parts can be permanently deformed if they are smashed out of shape during storage.

Inspect your respirator before each use, and inspect it again when you clean it. SCBAs must be inspected monthly. Air cylinders must be kept fully charged. Respirators kept for emergency use must be inspected each month and are to be stored in clearly marked compartments or covers.

Check how the respirator is functioning. Look at the condition of the facepiece, head straps, valves, connecting tube, cartridges, canisters, filters, etc. Make sure rubber parts are pliable and are not cracking. Have repairs made by a qualified person using manufacturer-approved parts. Get repairs done before you need to wear the respirator again.

Respirator Users Need Training

You must have training before any required respirator use. Retraining is required at least annually. Changes in the workplace can also trigger retraining. If you are using a respirator on a voluntary basis where contaminants are at a safe level, your employer has to provide you with basic information on respirator use.

Work at Working Safely

1. Only use respirators that have been selected to protect against the hazards.

2. When you put on a respirator, check its fit and operation.

3. Look for respirator damage or deterioration before and after use.

4. Respirators need to be cleaned, disinfected, and stored properly. Follow filter, cartridge, and canister change schedules.

Safe at Home

Your biggest need for the use of respiratory protection at home is likely to be when you create dust from cutting, sawing, and sanding wood, drywall, insulation, or other materials during home improvement projects. Other activities that could expose you to harmful dust and mold would be cleaning out old, musty, dusty items from crawl spaces, basements, attics, and garages. Using oil-based varnishes and paints, paint thinners, or other solvents can also expose you to harmful vapors.

Many hardware stores sell respirators. It's still best to use a NIOSH-approved respirator even if you aren't at work. Always follow the manufacturer's instructions for using a respirator properly, and consult with your physician to see if you may have any health problems that would prevent you from safely wearing a respirator.

Employee _____

Instructor _____

Date _____

Location _____

RESPIRATORY PROTECTION REVIEW

1. Worksite-specific procedures for the proper use of respirators are part of the:
   a. OSHA standard.
   b. Employer's respiratory protection program.
   c. Inspection procedures.
   d. Medical evaluation.

2. The two general types of respirators are:
   a. Tight-fitting and air line.
   b. Cartridge and self-contained.
   c. Filter and air-purifying.
   d. Atmosphere-supplying and air-purifying.

3. What type of respirator uses a filter or cartridge?
   a. Atmosphere-supplying.
   b. Air-purifying.
   c. Positive pressure.
   d. Pressure demand.

4. What type of respirator uses an airline?
   a. Self-contained breathing apparatus.
   b. Supplied-air respirator.
   c. Negative pressure.
   d. Dust mask.

5. Who evaluates an employee's physical ability to wear a respirator?
   a. The employee.
   b. The safety manager.
   c. A physician or other licensed health care professional.
   d. The employer.

6. Selecting the right type of respirator to use depends on if it will be used:
   a. In an atmosphere that's immediately dangerous to life or health.
   b. By more than one employee.
   c. During every shift.
   d. Only for short-term projects.

7. Which of the following isn't true about fit testing?
   a. Fit tests must be done at least annually.
   b. The type of fit test depends of the type of respirator.
   c. Employees who have facial hair between the facepiece and their skin may be fit tested.
   d. Fit tests are required for respirators that have a tight-fitting facepiece.

8. If you need to change a filter, cartridge, or canister while you are using the respirator:
   a. Always leave the respirator use area first.
   b. Wait until the end of your shift.
   c. Take off your respirator to make the change in the respirator use area.
   d. Have another medical evaluation after you make the change.

9. Each time you wear a respirator with a tight-fitting facepiece:
   a. Only do a positive pressure check if the respirator uses filters.
   b. Only do a negative pressure check if the respirator uses cartridges.
   c. Do both a positive pressure check and a negative pressure check.
   d. Have another full fit test.

10. If you notice that the facepiece has cracks in it:
    a. Get repairs done before you need to use the respirator again.
    b. Put some duct tape over the cracks.
    c. Change filters more often.
    d. Wait until your next annual fit test to have repairs made using approved parts.

SLIPS, TRIPS AND FALLS

On TV and in cartoons, a person falls but doesn't get a scratch. In reality, falls cause injury and lost time. Often, falls are fatal.

Injuries from falls may include cuts, bruises, sprains, strains, broken bones, and back injuries.

Where Are the Regulations?

The Occupational Safety and Health Administration (OSHA) has fall protection requirements at 29 CFR:

- Subpart D, Walking/Working Surfaces (1910.21 – .30).

- Subpart I, Personal Protective Equipment (PPE) (1910.132 and .140).

Physical Factors at Work in a Fall

It might seem that an accident due to a loss of balance is pretty uncomplicated. Actually, slips, trips, and falls involve three laws of science:

Friction is the resistance between things, such as between your shoes and the surface you walk on. Without it, you are likely to slip and fall. A good example is a slip on ice, where your shoes can't "grip" the surface. You lose traction and you fall.

Momentum is affected by the speed and size of the moving object. You've heard the expression, "The bigger they are, the harder they fall." Translate that to mean the more you weigh and the faster you are moving, the harder your fall will be if you should trip or slip.

Gravity is the force that pulls you to the ground once a fall starts. If you lose your balance and begin to fall, you're going to hit the ground. Your body has automatic systems for keeping its balance. Your eyes, ears, and muscles all work to keep your body close to its natural center of balance. A fall is likely if your center of balance (sometimes called center of gravity) shifts too far and can't be restored to normal.

What Happens When You Slip?

Slips can be caused by wet surfaces, spills, or weather hazards like ice and snow. Slips are more likely to occur when you hurry, run, or don't pay attention to where you're walking. Follow these safety precautions in order to avoid a slip:

- Practice safe walking skills. If you must walk on slippery or wet surfaces, take short steps to keep your center of balance under you, and move slowly. Devices such as strap-on cleats can be fastened to shoes or boots for greater traction on ice.

- Clean up spills right away. Even minor spills can be very hazardous. Report spills or leaks of hazardous materials to the proper authorities immediately.

- Don't let grease accumulate on a shop floor around machinery.

Properly Cleaned Floors Help

Floors must be dry and free of protruding objects such as nails, splinters, holes, or loose boards. Use floor finishes properly so they don't leave a slippery surface. Many slip accidents are caused by improper cleaning methods. Some floor finishes may have additives that help increase traction. If you're mopping or cleaning, post signs or place barricades to warn others of a wet surface.

Added Traction for Wet Floors

One way to avoid slips on frequently wet surfaces is to apply some type of abrasive that will increase traction. Epoxies and enamels that contain gritty compounds may be painted on floors. Adhesive-backed strips of skid-resistant material can be applied to some walking surfaces.

Rubber mats can be used as a permanent or temporary solution to wet areas.

What Happens When You Trip?

Trips occur whenever your foot hits an object and you are moving with enough momentum to be thrown off balance. Remember these rules to avoid tripping:

- Make sure you can see where you're going. Carry only loads that you can see over or around.

- Don't run up or down stairs or jump from landing to landing. Use the handrails.

- Keep work areas well-lit. Report burnt out light bulbs.

- Keep your work area clean, and don't clutter aisles or stairs. Store materials and tools properly.

- Arrange furniture so that it doesn't interfere with walkways or pedestrian traffic in your area.

- Keep extension or power tool cords out of walkways.

- Eliminate hazards due to loose footing on stairs, steps, and floors. Report loose carpeting, stair treads, hand rails, or floor tiles, and report broken pavement and floor boards.

What Happens When You Fall?

Falls occur whenever you move too far off your center of balance. Slips and trips often push you off your center of balance far enough for gravity to take over to cause a fall, but there are many other ways to fall. Falls are also caused by makeshift ladders, misuse of ladders, accidents while climbing, and improper scaffolding use.

A Few Words About Ladders

There are three main types of ladders:

- Portable,

- Fixed, and

- Mobile.

At 29 CFR 1910.23 OSHA outlines the requirements for ladders. It includes details on ladder design specifications and provides the following general requirements:

- Do not apply coatings that could hide ladder defects,

- The ladder surface must be free of puncture or cut hazards,

- Ladders must be used only for their designed purpose,

- Ladders must be inspected before use on each shift they're used (it's a good idea to give every ladder a good once-over before *each* use) and more frequently as necessary (for example, if a ladder tips over, you'll need to re-inspect it), and

- Defective ladders are to be immediately tagged "Dangerous: Do Not Use" and removed from service for repair or replacement.

Safe Use

When you follow safe climbing techniques you:

- Select a ladder having a load rating high enough to support you and your tools. If the ladder has a safety label, check it for the ladder's duty rating and other important information.

- Don't use a metal ladder if you're working near sources of electricity (choose fiberglass or wood instead).

- Position the ladder on a firm, level surface. Secure and stabilize the ladder to prevent it from moving while in use. If you're in a high-traffic area, or if the ladder itself could create a hazard for others, put up a temporary barricade, like cones or caution tape, to keep others away from the ladder while in use.

- Make sure spreaders and locking devices on stepstools, step ladders, or combination ladders are properly engaged. Never step on the top two steps of a stepladder.

- Follow the 4-to-1 rule for straight ladders and extension ladders. This means for every four feet of the ladder's length from the ground to its top support, you'll need to position the ladder out a foot from the wall. For example, for a working length of 16 feet, you will need four feet between the wall and the base of the ladder.

- Extend the side rails of a straight ladder or extension ladder at least three feet above the roof line to keep the ladder stable when it is used to access an upper landing surface.

- Never extend an extension ladder while a worker is on it.

- Ensure the bottom of your shoes are clean and dry and have good tread.

- Face the ladder when climbing up and down.

- Grasp the ladder with at least one hand at all times while climbing up and down. Have one hand and two feet, or two hands and one foot on the ladder at all times as you climb. This is what is known as maintaining three points of contact.

- Do not slide your hands up and down the side rails instead of grasping the ladder (this is considered to be unsafe).

- Do not carry anything that could cause you to lose your balance.

- Use a tool belt or back pack to carry items on the ladder or hoist them up to you after you're done climbing.

- Be sure you are still able to maintain your balance and have a firm grasp of the ladder if you need to carry a small item, like a hand tool.

- Keep your body within the ladder's rails.

Ladder Inspection

A damaged ladder may not be able to support its rated load, and it could collapse when you climb it. Some of the things you should look for when inspecting a ladder are:

- Sharp edges,
- Corrosion,
- Instability,
- Structural defects,
- Dents and bends, and
- Loose or missing fittings.

Ladder Storage

Ladders should be stored in designated areas where they are generally protected from the elements. Extreme weather, including excessive temperatures or direct sunlight, can negatively affect the strength of some materials. It's best to store ladders on racks or hooks, and secure them so they will not be knocked over.

Ladder Training

Under OSHA's requirements at 29 CFR 1910.30, you must be trained on the proper care, inspection, use, and storage of the ladders you will use. You'll need retraining when workplace changes or changes to the types of ladders used make your earlier training obsolete. You'll also need retraining if your employer determines you no longer demonstrate the knowledge or skills to use ladders safely.

Scaffolds Can Be Dangerous

Scaffolds are elevated work platforms that may be built up from the ground or suspended from above. The applicable scaffold regulations are found in OSHA's construction rules at 29 CFR 1926.450 – .454. You must receive proper training before you work on a scaffold.

OSHA expects all scaffolds to be constructed according to the manufacturer's instructions. The agency also requires the installation of guardrail systems along all open sides and ends of platforms, use of guardrail systems and/or personal fall arrest systems for scaffolds more than 10 feet above a lower level, and safe work practices.

When working from a scaffold, take these safety precautions:

- Make sure the scaffold is far enough from power lines.

- Your employer's competent person must inspect all scaffolds and scaffold components for visible defects at the start of each work shift and after any incident that could affect a scaffold's structure.

- Do not work on a scaffold covered with snow, ice, or other slippery material, except to remove the material.

- Do not work on a scaffold during a storm or high winds, unless your competent person says it is safe to do so and you are protected by a personal fall arrest system or wind screen.

- Do not load the scaffold more than its maximum intended load or rated capacity, whichever is less. Know this rating and know how to estimate the load (workers, tools, paint buckets, etc.) on the scaffold.

- Do not move the scaffold horizontally while anyone is on it, unless it has been designed to be moved during use.

- Make sure swinging loads being hoisted onto or near your scaffold have tag lines or other measures to control the load.

- Do not allow debris to accumulate on your scaffold.

- Do not use makeshift devices such as boxes and barrels to increase your working height. Do not increase your working height with a ladder except on large area scaffolds.

Reporting Hazards

Reporting fall hazards is integral to any effective safety effort. Report unsafe equipment, conditions, or procedures.

Work at Working Safely

Preventing slips, trips, and falls is a task that depends on many factors — most importantly — you. You can recognize and report hazards, work to eliminate hazards, and follow the safe procedures you learned in training. Take these precautions as you work:

1. Move carefully on stairs, in hallways, aisles, and work areas.

2. Report hazards like debris left in aisles, poor lighting, spills, and broken stairs.

3. Learn how to use ladders and scaffolding safely.

4. Use guardrails on walks, runways, or platforms four feet or more from ground level.

Remember that falls are a leading cause of injuries. They aren't funny — preventing them is serious business.

Safe at Home

Slips, trips, and falls can happen at home just as easily as they can at work. Follow some of the same precautions to prevent injuries from slips, trips, and falls:

- Wipe up spills right away to keep floors dry;

- Clear snow and ice from walkways, and spread salt or sand as needed;

- Place mats at doorways;

- Keep floors clean;

- Keep halls and stairways well lit and clear of clutter; and

- Promptly repair loose carpeting and floor tiles.

A fall from a ladder can cause a serious injury or a fatality. To stay safe when something is out of your reach:

- Use a ladder instead of climbing on furniture.

- Inspect the ladder for damage before you use it.

- Use the ladder as it was intended to be used. Open stepladders fully and lock the spreader bars in place. Make sure a straight ladder or an extension ladder is long enough so that you can set it up using the 4-to-1 rule and have three feet above the top support point.

- Set up the ladder on a firm, stable, solid base.

- Face the ladder, keep your hands free, and have at least one hand always grasping the ladder as you climb up and down.

- Stay off the top step of a stepladder and the top rungs of a straight or extension ladder.

- Position the ladder so you can easily reach materials without having to reach dangerously out to the side.

For big home improvement projects, set up a proper scaffold instead of using ladders and planks to imitate one. The costs will far exceed the scaffold's rental fee if someone falls from a makeshift scaffold.

Employee _____

Instructor _____

Date _____

Location _____

SLIPS, TRIPS, AND FALLS REVIEW

1. Slips are more likely to occur when you don't pay attention to where you're walking or when you:
   a. Clean up spills right away.
   b. Hurry or run.
   c. Keep your balance and move slowly.
   d. Use proper cleaning methods and floor finishes.

2. One way to avoid tripping is to:
   a. Step over loose floor tiles.
   b. Make sure extension cords running across walkways are bright yellow.
   c. Make sure you can see where you're going.
   d. Apply adhesive skid-resistant strips to stair treads.

3. If the job calls for a ladder:
   a. Stand on a chair if it's more convenient.
   b. Use any ladder you can find; even if it's damaged.
   c. Use a ladder that's in good condition.
   d. Climb up a stack of boxes.

4. What should you do if the ladder you have isn't tall enough for the job?
   a. Stand on the top step or rung of the ladder and reach up.
   b. Set up the ladder on some boxes to make it taller.
   c. Get a taller ladder.
   d. Climb up on furniture or shelves if they're tall enough.

5. The three laws of science involved in a fall are friction, _____, and gravity.
   a. Momentum.
   b. Focus.
   c. Size.
   d. Coordination.

6. _____ can occur when gravity takes over if you move too far off your center of balance.
   a. Slips.
   b. Trips.
   c. Falls.
   d. None of the above.

7. _____ can occur when there is too little friction between your feet and the surface you walk or work on.
   a. Slips.
   b. Trips.
   c. Falls.
   d. None of the above.

8. _____ can occur when your foot hits an object while you are walking.
   a. Slips.
   b. Trips.
   c. Falls.
   d. None of the above.

9. Climbing a _____ can cause a fall.
   a. Defective ladder.
   b. Hill.
   c. Standard stairway.
   d. None of the above.

10. If you spill your soda in an aisle:
   a. Cover it with a rubber mat.
   b. Wipe it up right away.
   c. Report it to the maintenance department.
   d. Both a. and c.

TOOL SAFETY

Everyone is familiar with common, everyday tools, but don't take them for granted.

Avoid Tool Injuries

Crushed hands and arms, severed fingers, blindness — the list of possible machinery-related injuries is as long as it is horrifying. There seem to be as many hazards created by moving machine parts as there are types of machines. And, commonly used portable tools also cause serious injuries. Even hand tools cause injuries. Too frequently, tool use causes serious eye injuries, lacerations, fractures, burns, and minor scrapes, cuts, or bruises.

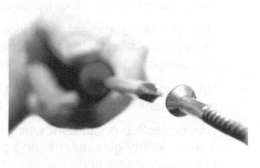

In addition, most machines and power tools are powered by electricity. Electrical hazards are equally harmful.

General Tool Safety Rules

Injuries can be prevented by keeping tools in good condition, using the right tool for the job, using the tool properly, and wearing required personal protective equipment.

* Keep your work area well lit, clean, and dry.

* Stand where you have firm footing and good balance while you use any tools.

* Arrange the work and use portable tools so that the tool will move away from your hands and body if it slips.

* Make sure that the material you are working on is held securely — use clamps or a vise if you need to.

- Use the right tool for the job. Don't force a small tool to do heavy-duty work.

- Regularly inspect tools, cords, and accessories. Repair or replace problem equipment immediately.

- Never use a dull blade or cutting edge.

- Keep electric cables and cords clean and free from kinks. Never carry a tool by its cord.

- Use all guards and safety devices (i.e., three-prong plugs, double-insulated tools, and safety switches) that are designed to be used with the equipment.

- Dress right. Never wear clothing or jewelry that could become entangled in machinery or power tools.

- Use protective equipment when necessary. This might include safety glasses, hearing protection, and respiratory protection.

- Make adjustments and accessory changes when machinery is turned off and unplugged.

- Concentrate — don't take your eyes off your work or talk to anyone as you use tools.

- Maintain your tools. Keep them sharp, oiled, and stored in a safe, dry place.

- Install or repair equipment only if you're qualified. A faulty job may cause fires or seriously injure you or other workers.

Good tool habits soon become second nature. Follow the tool safety guidelines at your workplace and the equipment you operate will serve you efficiently and safely.

Select the Tool You Need

Use durable tools made from good quality materials. Metal tools should have working points that resist bending, cracking, chipping, or excessive wear from normal use. Handles should be made of durable material that does not crack or splinter easily if the tool is dropped or hit.

Pay extra attention to any hand tools that you will be using around exposed electrical parts. Make sure that the handle is electrically insulated and rated to handle the voltage. If you need to use tools to work in areas where flammable liquids are stored or used, hand tools must be made from non-sparking alloys and power tools must be approved for the hazard in order to prevent sparks that can ignite flammable vapors.

Personal Protective Equipment

Engineering controls eliminate the hazard at the source. But whenever engineering controls are not available or are not fully capable of protecting you, you must wear protective clothing or personal protective equipment (PPE).

Always wear safety glasses when using hammers, chisels, wire cutters, crowbars, bolt cutters, saws, drills, grinders, or any tool that could create chips, pieces, or sparks. If machine coolants could splash, then face shields and safety goggles might be necessary. Wear cut-resistant gloves when handling knives or other sharp-edged hand tools. Caps and hair nets can help keep your hair from being caught in machinery. Hearing protection may be needed when operating noisy machines.

It is important to note that PPE and other clothing can create hazards. Protective gloves can become caught in rotating parts. Loose-fitting shirts might possibly become entangled. Jewelry can catch on machine parts and lead to serious injury by pulling a hand into the danger area.

Use the Right Hand Tool the Right Way

Look at your hand tools. Their shape and design shows you how they are intended to be used.

Knives. Using knives as pries, screwdrivers, can openers, awls, or punches can easily damage the blade. A sharp blade needs less pressure to cut and has less of a chance of getting hung up and slipping. Always move the blade away from you as you cut.

Screwdrivers. Using screwdrivers as pries, can openers, punches, chisels, wedges, etc. can cause chipped, rounded, bent, dull tips; bent shafts; and split or broken handles. If the screwdriver tip doesn't fit the screw, you'll apply more force and the screwdriver can easily slip. Redress the tips of flat head screwdrivers to keep them sharp and square edged. Screwdrivers with shorter shafts give you better control. Screwdrivers with thicker handles apply more torque, with less effort on your part.

Hammers and Mallets. Nail hammers are designed to drive nails. Ball pein hammers are designed for striking cold chisels and metal punches. Mallets have a striking head of plastic, wood, or rawhide and are designed for striking 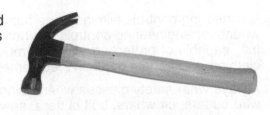 wood chisels, punches, or dies. Sledgehammers are for striking concrete or stone. You can damage a hammer by trying to use it for the wrong purpose. Don't use a hammer with a mushroomed striking surface or a loose handle. You can damage other tools by trying to force them by hitting them with a hammer.

Pliers. Don't substitute a pliers for a wrench. The face of the pliers is not designed to grip a fastener, and the pliers can easily slip off of the nut or bolt. Pliers are designed for gripping so you can more easily bend or pull material. They'll provide a strong grip if you protect them from getting bent out of  shape and keep the gripping surface from being damaged.

Cutters. Use cutters or snips to remove banding wire or strapping. Trying to use a pry bar to snap open banding can cause injuries. Keep the cutting edges sharp and protect them from getting nicked or gouged.

Wrenches. Use adjustable open-ended wrenches for light-duty jobs when the proper sized wrench isn't available. Position yourself so you will be pulling the wrench towards you, with the open end facing you — this lessens the chance of the wrench slipping off of the fastener when you apply force. Select an open-ended wrench to fit the fastener for medium-duty jobs. With the snug fit, these wrenches can apply more force than an adjustable open-ended wrench. Again, pull the wrench with the open end facing you to avoid slippage. Box and socket wrenches should be used when a heavy pull is required. Because they completely encircle the fastener, they apply even pressure with a minimal chance of slipping. Some box wrenches are designed for heavy-duty use, and they do have a striking surface. But, in general, don't try to increase the torque by hitting the wrench with a hammer or by adding a cheater bar to the wrench's handle — this can break or damage the wrench. If the fastener is too tight, use some penetrating oil to lubricate it.

Wood Saws. For cutting wood, use a cross-cut saw to cut across the grain, and use a ripping saw to cut with the grain. Select a saw with coarse teeth for sawing green wood, thick lumber, or for making coarse cuts. Fine-toothed saws can be used to make fine cuts in dry wood. After use, wipe the saw with a lightly oiled rag to keep the teeth clean. Protect the saw from getting bent or damaged in storage.

Metalworking Hand Tools. Hack saws should have the blade installed with the teeth facing forward, and apply pressure on the forward stroke. Use a light pressure to avoid twisting and breaking the blade. Metal files need to be kept clean and protected from damage. Hitting the file against a hard object to clean it can damage the file — use a file card for cleaning.

Respect Portable Power Tools

Saws. The circular saw is a heavy-duty tool with interchangeable blades for all types of woodcutting. The saber saw is somewhat smaller and used for smaller woodcutting jobs and curved cuts. A chainsaw may be either gasoline or electrically powered. Before cutting, inspect the material to be cut for nails or foreign objects. Make sure blade guards are in place and working properly. Stay alert!

Saws are noisy and the sound may drown out warning shouts or instructions. Wear goggles or goggles and a face shield to protect yourself from flying debris or sawdust. Inspect the blade regularly. First, turn the saw off and unplug it. Don't use dull or loose blades. Don't overload the motor by pushing too hard or cutting material that is too heavy. Be sure you have firm footing and balance when using any saw. Slips or falls can be deadly when you're holding a power tool.

Drills. Variable speed drills are versatile tools used for boring holes, turning screws, buffing, and grinding. Select the correct drill bit for the job to be done. Use only sharp bits. Make sure the material being drilled is secured or clamped firmly. Hold the drill firmly and at the correct angle. Don't force it to work or lean on it with all your strength. Always remove the bit from the drill when you're finished. Use a drill bit sharpener to maintain the cutting edge on drill bits.

Grinding Wheels. Bench grinders are useful for sharpening, shaping, and smoothing metal, wood, plastic, or stone. Keep machine guards in place and wear hearing and eye protection. Before use, make sure that wheels are firmly held on spindles and work rests are tight. Stand to one side while starting the motor, until the operating speed is reached — this prevents injury if a defective wheel breaks apart. Use light pressure when you start grinding — too much on a cold wheel may cause failure.

Sanders. Two types of sanders are orbital and belt. Arrange the cord so that it won't be damaged by the abrasive belt. Keep both hands on the tool for good control. Hold onto the sander when you plug it in. Clean dust and chips from the motor and vent holes regularly and lubricate when necessary.

Impact Wrenches. They operate on electricity or compressed air and deliver extra power and torque for fastening and loosening bolts and drilling. Don't force a wrench to take on a job bigger than it's designed to handle. Don't use standard hand sockets or driver parts with an impact tool. Don't reverse direction of rotation while the trigger is depressed.

Soldering Irons or "Guns." They can be dangerous because of the heat they generate. Handle with care — they can easily cause serious burns. Always assume that a soldering iron is hot. Rest a heated iron on a rack or metal surface. Never swing an iron to remove solder. Hold small soldering jobs with pliers, never in your hand. Wait until the tool is cool before you put it away.

Propane and Gas Torches. These commonly used tools pose fire and heat hazards. Never use a flame to test for propane or gas leaks. Never store the fuel tanks in an unventilated area, and never use a tank with a leaking valve. Use torches in well-ventilated areas. Avoid breathing the vapors and fumes they generate.

Glue Guns. A glue gun can be a real time saver. However, because it generates temperatures as high as 450°F, avoid contact with the hot nozzle and glue.

Shop Vacuums. Clean filters regularly and never use your vacuum to pick up flammable liquids or smoldering materials.

Use Stationary Machinery Safely

Table Saw. This saw has a large circular blade used to make a variety of cuts in wood or other material. Never reach over the saw to push stock. Stand slightly to one side, never in line with the saw. A "kickback" occurs when material being cut is thrown back toward the operator. This is one of the greatest hazards in running a table saw. To avoid it:

- Never use a dull blade.

- Don't cut "freehand" or attempt to rip badly warped wood.

- Use the splitter guard.

- Don't drop wood on an unguarded saw.

Radial-Arm Saw. Often called the number one multipurpose saw in the shop, this saw blade is mounted on a moveable head, and slides in tracks or along a shaft. Most have built-in safety devices such as key switches to start them, blade guards, anti-kickback pawls, and blade brakes. The saw and motor should always be returned to the rear of the table against the column after a cut is made.

Drill Press. The stationary drill press is a larger, more powerful version of a portable drill. Clamp or securely fasten the material being drilled whenever possible. Make sure any attachments are fastened tightly.

Power Sanders. Always select the correct grade of abrasive for the job. Move the work around to avoid heating and burning a portion of the disk, belt, or wood. Remember to use the dust collector if the sander has one.

Shapers. A shaper is used mainly for grooving and fluting woods. It can be dangerous because of its high speed and because the cutters are difficult to guard completely. When using a shaper, avoid loose clothing, wear eye protection, and make sure the cutters are sharp and securely fastened.

Welding Machines. The high-intensity arc of even a small welding machine can cause severe burns. Flame-resistant clothing and hand and eye protection are needed to protect against hot sparks and molten metal. Keep the area around the welding operation clean — hot sparks can start fires.

Work at Working Safely

Proper care and safety when using tools and machinery is vital.

1. Respect your equipment, know the dangers it presents, and take safety precautions necessary to work without injury.

2. Take out only the tools that you will need for the job. Piles of extra tools can get in the way or get lost.

3. Always wear appropriate personal protective equipment.

4. Maintain tools and equipment with regular servicing and good housekeeping practices. Putting tools away after use keeps them from getting damaged or disappearing.

5. If you don't know how to use a particular tool, don't be afraid to admit it. Find someone who does and learn from an experienced worker.

6. Carry your tools safely. Use a tool box or a tool chest to move tools around. If you need to carry tools, especially on a ladder, wear a tool belt.

Safe at Home

The same precautions for safe tool use apply whether you're at home or at work:

- Follow the general tool safety rules outlined in this chapter.

- Use the right tool for the job.

- Wear personal protective equipment.

- Follow the tool manufacturer's instructions on the correct way to use the tool.

- Inspect tools for damage before use. When you use an electric power tool, be sure to inspect the cord and plug for any damage. Don't use damaged, unsafe tools.

- Keep your tools clean, and follow the tool manufacturer's instructions for proper maintenance.

Employee _____

Instructor _____

Date _____

Location _____

TOOL SAFETY REVIEW

1. All of the following are general tool safety rules except:
   a. Keeping tools in good condition.
   b. Arranging the work so a tool will move toward you if it slips.
   c. Wearing required personal protective equipment.
   d. Making sure the material being worked on is held securely.

2. If tools are used in areas where flammable liquids are stored or used:
   a. It's safe to use any type of hand tool.
   b. Use electrical power tools made from non-sparking alloys.
   c. Use electrical power tools that are approved for the hazard.
   d. No extra precautions are needed.

3. If using a hand tool could create chips, pieces, or sparks:
   a. Stand so the tool moves away from you.
   b. Wear safety glasses.
   c. Wear a cap to keep clean.
   d. None of the above.

4. A flat-head screwdriver:
   a. Should also be used as a pry or wedge.
   b. Can be damaged if it isn't used properly.
   c. Is still safe to use if it doesn't fit the screw.
   d. Is safer if the head has rounded corners.

5. Mallets are designed for striking:
   a. Nails.
   b. Metal punches.
   c. Wood chisels.
   d. Concrete.

6. Pliers can easily slip off of a nut or bolt:
   a. If you aren't using enough force.
   b. If they aren't kept properly oiled.
   c. If you don't inspect them before each use.
   d. When you try to use them as a wrench.

7. For a heavy pull on a nut:
   a. Use an open-ended wrench with the opening facing you.
   b. Use an open-ended wrench with the opening facing away from you.
   c. Add a "cheater bar" to an open-ended wrench to get more torque.
   d. Use a box wrench or a socket wrench.

8. To cut wood along the grain:
   a. Use a ripping saw.
   b. Use a cross-cut saw.
   c. Use a fine-tooth saw if the wood is green.
   d. Use any saw, even if it's slightly damaged.

9. Use light pressure when you start using a grinding wheel:
   a. So that you get the feel of the tool.
   b. If the work rest is loose.
   c. Because too much pressure on a cold wheel could cause it to fail.
   d. None of the above.

10. When you use a variable speed drill, do all of the following except:
    a. Use sharp bits.
    b. Be sure the material being drilled is secured in place.
    c. Hold the drill at the correct angle.
    d. Leave the bit in the drill when you're done using it.

VIOLENCE IN THE WORKPLACE

Workplace violence can range from verbal or physical threats or intimidation to assault and battery. Workplace assaults result in thousands of injuries and hundreds of fatalities each year. The Occupational Safety and Health Administration (OSHA), the National Institute for Occupational Safety and Health (NIOSH), the United States Office of Personnel Management, and several states have issued guidelines and preventative strategies for the control of workplace violence. This chapter will suggest ways for you to prevent violence at your job and ways to respond to violence if it should occur.

Sources of Violence

Occasionally, violence occurs from within an organization. When disputes among co-workers, supervisors, and management go unresolved, arguments, threats, harassment, vandalism, arson, assault, or other violent acts can be the result.

The greatest risk of work-related homicide comes from violence inflicted by third parties, such as robbers and muggers. Risks have been identified with workplaces involved in dealing with the public; exchanging money or guarding valuables; delivering passengers, goods, or services; working out of a mobile worksite (taxicab or police cruiser); working with unstable or volatile persons in health care or social service settings; working late at night or early in the morning; working alone or in small numbers; or working in high crime areas.

Recognize Potentially Violent Situations

Learn to recognize situations that could result in violence. Often a co-worker, customer, or client will express troubled feelings before becoming angry or violent. Many times, listening and concern is all that is needed at the early stages of trouble. If you sense that the problem will get worse, or if someone threatens you, take it seriously and report the incident to your supervisor.

Be aware of places where an assailant could hide, and be leery of someone who is loitering or does not belong in the workplace.

Take Preventative Measures

When you have to work alone or in a small isolated group, use the "buddy system" or ask for an escort. Radios or cellular phones can help you to stay in touch. If you travel between work sites, call to check in so your co-workers know where you are, and keep your vehicle well maintained to avoid breakdowns. When walking to your vehicle, have your keys ready, stay in well lit areas, appear confident, and avoid hiding spots or threatening strangers. Look in and around your vehicle before getting in, and lock your doors before you start your vehicle. If you are followed or threatened along the way, keep going to the closest safe area to report the threat to the police.

Many workplaces have key-card access systems and have employees wear identification badges. Visitors have to check in to get a pass before they are allowed inside. Know who is, and who isn't, supposed to be in your work area. If you are working with the public, limit your customers or clients to using doorways that can be seen by workers.

Maintain good visibility in your workplace. Windows and mirrors help eliminate hiding spots. Windows also help police or security guards to see in and check on your safety. Good lighting inside and out will deter criminals.

Video cameras, alarms, metal detectors, and security patrols reduce crime. Use drop safes and post signs to show that little cash is on-hand. Vary the schedules for money drops and pickups to make it harder on robbers. Keep valuable personal items locked up or at home. Counters and windows act as physical barriers between workers and potential attackers.

Handling a Violent Situation

If you become involved in a violent situation:

- Report threats or suspicious activity to your supervisors or the police. Keep your distance from the situation. Stay safe, and let the authorities handle it.

- If you are confronted, talk to the person. Stay calm, maintain eye contact, stall for time, and cooperate. If you are threatened by a weapon, freeze in place. Never try to grab a weapon.

- Attempts for escape from a confrontation should be to the closest secure area where you can quickly contact others and get help.

- Telephoned threats, like any threat, must be taken seriously. Write down as much detail as you can about the caller — accent, pitch of voice, background noise, etc. Immediately report the call to your supervisors or the police.

After Violence Occurs

Any violent act upsets people. Think ahead to have a plan on how to react after a violent incident. Some items that your organization will want to be prepared for are:

- Getting medical attention for anyone who was hurt during the incident.

- Reporting the incident to supervisors and/or the police.

- Securing the area so evidence is not disturbed.

- Identifying witnesses and interviewing them to get detailed notes on what happened.

- Analyzing what happened and making plans to prevent it from being repeated.

- Conducting employee assistance counseling or debriefing sessions to help employees reduce stress and fear so they can better understand and handle the situation.

Work at Working Safely

1. Follow your facility's security guidelines.

2. Report suspicious activity. Don't take matters into your own hands.

3. Take steps for personal safety when you're alone or at risk.

4. Stay calm in a violent situation.

5. After a violent incident, talk about it to reduce stress and fear.

Employee _____

Instructor _____

Date _____

Location _____

VIOLENCE IN THE WORKPLACE REVIEW

1. Verbal threats:
   a. Will always lead to physical assault.
   b. Are a form of workplace violence.
   c. Are not a form of workplace violence.
   d. Will never lead to physical assault.

2. Third-parties, such as robbers and muggers:
   a. Are the source of the greatest risk of work-related homicide.
   b. Cause more fatalities that vehicle crashes.
   c. Are only a risk in a warehouse setting.
   d. Are only a risk in areas with high crime rates.

3. To help improve security, many workplaces:
   a. Require a visitor to obtain a pass.
   b. Have key-card access systems.
   c. Have workers wear identification badges.
   d. All of the above.

4. All of the following methods deter criminals except:
   a. Having good visibility to eliminate hiding spots.
   b. Allowing customers or clients to enter through any doorway.
   c. Installing video cameras.
   d. Posting signs to show that little cash is on-hand.

5. If you witness suspicious activity that could become violent, do all of the following except:
   a. Report it to your supervisors or the police.
   b. Confront the person to find out what's going on.
   c. Let the authorities handle the situation.
   d. Keep your distance.

VIOLENCE

6. To help you stay in touch if you work alone or in a small isolated group:
   a. Use a phone to check in with coworkers.
   b. Ask for an escort in parking lots.
   c. Test the burglar alarm before your shift.
   d. None of the above.

7. To avoid the risk of becoming a victim of violence if you travel on the job:
   a. Assume the vehicle won't break down.
   b. Stay in the shadows to remain less visible when walking at night.
   c. Go to the closest safe area to report any threats to the police.
   d. Keep your vehicle unlocked so you can enter it quickly.

8. Risks for violence have been found in workplaces that:
   a. Handle money.
   b. Have a mobile worksite.
   c. Work late at night or early in the morning.
   d. All of the above.

9. After a violent incident, get medical attention for anyone who was injured, and:
   a. Report the incident to supervisors and/or the police.
   b. Pick up all of the evidence you can find.
   c. Encourage people to leave the area so they stay safe.
   d. All of the above.

10. After a violent incident:
   a. Talk about it to help reduce stress and fear.
   b. Stop following your facility's security guidelines until they're improved.
   c. Take matters into your own hands if it happens again.
   d. Become angry if someone threatens you.

WELDING, CUTTING, AND BRAZING

Gas fumes, radiation, and electric shock are very real hazards that you face on the job as a welder. Think about it — a welding arc is hot enough to melt steel, and the light it emits is literally blinding. It generates toxic fumes that are composed of microscopic particles of molten metal. Sparks and molten slag thrown by the arc can fly up to 35 feet and can cause fires and explosions.

Are you doomed to be injured if you are a welder? The job can be safe if you take the proper precautions and follow safe work practices.

Where Are the Regulations?

The Occupational Safety and Health Administration (OSHA) has developed rules governing welding, cutting, and brazing. These regulations are found at 29 CFR 1910.251 through .255 in Subpart Q. Your employer must train you to operate your welding equipment safely and to understand the welding process so that you perform your welding tasks safely.

What Are the Hazards?

Whenever welding, cutting, or brazing occurs, everyone involved in the operation must take precautions to prevent fires, explosions, or personal injuries.

There are three basic types of welding operations:

- **Oxygen-fuel gas welding** joins metal parts by generating extremely high heat during combustion.

- **Resistance welding** joins metals by generating heat through resistance created to the flow of electric current.

- **Arc welding** joins or cuts metal parts by heat generated from an electric arc that extends between the welding electrode and the electrode placed on the equipment being welded.

These common hazards are associated with welding:

- Eyes and skin can be damaged from exposure to ultraviolet and infrared rays produced by electric arcs and gas flames.

- Closed containers that once held flammables or combustibles can explode under high heat (proper cleaning and purging procedures must be followed before hot-work is started).

- Toxic gases, fumes, and dust may be released during welding and cutting operations.

- Welding or cutting near combustible or flammable materials creates a fire hazard.

- Metal splatter and electric shock cause injuries.

Compressed Gas Cylinders

A primary danger for oxygen-fuel gas welding operations stems from welding with compressed gas cylinders (CGCs) containing oxygen and acetylene. If CGCs are damaged, gas can escape with great force and the vessel itself can explode. Rocketing occurs when a CGC ruptures or is damaged. The cylinder can then act like a rocket with enough force to break through concrete walls.

Look for these danger signals when handling CGCs:

- Leaking (you may be able to hear or smell escaping gas).

- Corrosion.

- Cracks or burn marks.

- Contaminated valves.

- Worn or corroded hoses.

- Broken gauges or regulators.

Non-Flammable Compressed Gases

Non-flammable compressed gases do not catch fire easily or burn quickly. However, they possess other hazards. The cylinder label and SDS will tell you about toxic properties and physical hazards. Ammonia, argon, carbon dioxide, nitrogen, oxygen, chlorine, and nitrous oxide are all non-flammable compressed gases. These gases may:

- Cause dizziness, unconsciousness, or suffocation.

- Explode or accelerate fires if mishandled or exposed to high heat.

- Be harmful or toxic if inhaled.

- Irritate eyes, nose, throat, and lungs.

Flammable Compressed Gases

Flammable compressed gases have dangers besides those of high pressure. These gases can easily catch fire and burn rapidly. Flammable compressed gases include acetylene, hydrogen, natural gas, and propane.

Flammable compressed gases have the same dangers as non-flammable compressed gases, as well as:

- Ignition from heat, sparks, flames.

- Flash back if vapors travel to an ignition source.

Follow Safe Welding Practices

Here are a few
practices for working
safely that apply in
many situations.

- When working
  above ground or
  floor level, use a
  platform with
  toeboards and
  standard railings,
  or use a safety
  harness and
  lifeline. Also
  protect workers
  from stray sparks
  or slag in the area
  below an elevated surface where welding is taking
  place.

- Aim the welding torch away from cement or stone
  surfaces. Moisture within these materials could cause
  them to explode when they reach a certain temperature.

- When finished welding or cutting, warn other workers of
  hot metal by marking or putting up a sign. Keep floors
  clean by putting electrode or rod stubs in an appropriate
  container.

- Never use bare conductors, damaged regulators,
  torches, electrode holders, or other defective equipment.

- Do not arc or resistance weld while standing on damp
  surfaces.

Handling Compressed Gas Cylinders

The following procedures will reduce hazards of handling
CGCs:

- Identify a gas and its dangers before you use it. You can
  find this information on labels, safety data sheets, and
  cylinder markings. If you don't know what's in a cylinder,
  don't use it.

- When accepting an acetylene delivery, make sure it arrived upright. Acetylene cylinders contain a stabilizing liquid that may have leaked from a horizontal cylinder.

- Make sure valves, hoses, connectors, and regulators are in good condition.

- Keep oil and grease away from oxygen CGCs, valves, and hoses. If your hands, gloves, or clothing are oily, do not handle oxygen CGCs. Oxygen makes materials more flammable. Oxygen and compressed air are not the same thing. Do not use them interchangeably.

- Check to see if regulators, hoses, and gauges can be used with different gases. Assume they cannot.

- Never open valves until regulators are drained of gas and pressure-adjusting devices are released. When opening CGCs, point outlets away from people and sources of ignition. Open valves slowly. On valves without hand wheels, use only supplier-recommended wrenches. On valves with hand wheels, never use wrenches. Never hammer a hand wheel to open or close a valve.

- When empty, close and return CGCs. Empty CGCs must be marked "MT" or "Empty." Empty acetylene CGCs **must** be so labeled.

Here are several things to remember when moving CGCs:

- Don't drop or bang CGCs.

- Don't roll, drag, or slide CGCs.

- You may carefully roll CGCs along the bottom rim for short distances.

- Don't lift CGCs by the cap unless using hand trucks so designed.

- Ropes and chains should only be used if a CGC has special lugs to accommodate this.

- Some CGCs may require special hand trucks.

Remember these guidelines when storing CGCs:

- When in storage, keep the steel protective cap screwed on. This step reduces the chance that a blow to the valve will allow gas to escape.

- Store cylinders upright.

- Group cylinders by types of gas.

- Store full and empty cylinders apart.

- Store gases so that old stock is removed and used first.

- To keep cylinders from falling over, secure them with chains or cables. (But never secure CGCs to conduit carrying electrical wiring.)

- Make sure fire extinguishers near the storage area are appropriate for gases stored there.

- Store oxygen CGCs at least 20 feet from flammables or combustibles, or separate them by a 5 foot, fire-resistant barrier.

Equipment Inspection and Maintenance

It almost goes without saying that welding equipment should be used according to the manufacturer's instructions. You must be familiar with the correct use and limitations of your welding equipment. In addition, routinely inspect and maintain your welding equipment, including welding cylinders. Inspect cylinders regularly to make sure all parts are in good working order, especially manifolds, distribution piping, portable outlet headers, regulators, hose, and hose connections.

Ventilation

Ventilation techniques vary depending on the size and type of the industry you work in. Some large facilities use sophisticated industrial exhaust systems like state-of-the-art electrostatic precipitators. Very often, however, a relatively simple ventilation method like the appropriate use of wall fans will be all that is required to provide good ventilation during welding operations.

Be aware that general ventilation should never be relied on as the only means of protection when air contaminants are toxic. Where ventilation is poor, you may need to use a respirator.

Fire Prevention

You must do your welding in places safe from fire hazards. All fire hazards in the vicinity of a welding or cutting operation must be moved to a safe place before welding may begin.

When neither the object to be welded nor the fire hazards near it can be moved, guards must be set up to confine heat, sparks, and slag. Under these circumstances, your employer must issue a written authorization, or **hot work permit**, outlining the conditions under which the welding may occur.

Your employer must designate a worker as a fire watch whenever welding or cutting is performed in locations where other than a minor fire might develop or when any of the following conditions exist:

- Appreciable combustible material, in building construction or contents, is closer than 35 feet to the point of operation.

- Appreciable combustibles are more than 35 feet away but are easily ignited by sparks.

- Wall or floor openings within a 35-foot radius expose combustible material in adjacent areas including concealed spaces in walls or floors.

- Combustible materials are adjacent to the opposite side of metal partitions, walls, ceilings, or roofs and are likely to be ignited by conduction or radiation.

Fire watches must:

- Have fire extinguishing equipment readily available and be trained in its use.

- Be familiar with facilities for sounding an alarm in the event of a fire.

- Watch for fires in all exposed areas.

- Try to extinguish fires only when obviously within the capacity of the equipment available, or otherwise sound the alarm.

- Be maintained for at least a half-hour after completion of welding or cutting operations to detect and extinguish possible smoldering fires.

Confined Spaces

Welding or cutting in a confined space presents its own hazards. Follow permit-required confined space entry and rescue procedures. In addition:

- Evaluate the space for its limited work area, any hazardous atmosphere, or a slippery floor surface. Evaluate the space for flammability or combustibility hazards and for toxic fumes that could result from the welding process.

- Perform atmospheric testing for oxygen deficiency and for toxic and flammable or combustible gases before and during entry. If the tests show that flammable or combustible gases are present, the space must be ventilated until safe to enter. If the atmosphere is toxic and cannot be cleared through ventilation, appropriate respiratory protection equipment must be used. All energy sources that could cause employee injury must be disconnected and locked in the "off" position before entry.

- When working in confined spaces wear a safety harness attached to a lifeline. An attendant must tend the lifeline to observe the welder and initiate emergency rescue procedures.

- If hot work inside the space is interrupted, special precautions should be implemented. Disconnect power to arc welding or cutting units and remove the electrode from the holder. Turn off torch valves and shut off the gas supply to gas welding or cutting units at a point outside. Remove the torch and hose from the space, if possible. Cylinders for welding operations should never be placed in confined spaces.

Use PPE When Welding

It's important for welders to wear flame-retardant clothing and personal protective equipment. Necessary protective gear may include the following, depending on the job:

- Aprons — flame resistant (leather or other material that protects against radiated heat and sparks).

- Leggings — leather or similar protection.

- Safety shoes — ankle length (low cut shoes may catch slag).

- Protection during overhead work — shoulder cape or cover, skull cap made of leather or other protective material, other flame resistant cap worn under helmet.

- Ear protection — ear plugs, and, on very noisy jobs like high velocity plasma torches, ear muffs.

- Head protection — safety helmet or other head gear to protect against falling objects.

- Eye and face protection — operators, welders, or helpers should wear goggles, a helmet, and face shield to provide maximum protection for the particular welding or cutting process used. All filter lenses and plates must meet the test for transmission of radiant energy prescribed in ANSI Standard Z87.1, *Practice for Occupational and Educational Eye and Face Protection*.

- Respiratory protection — If gases, dusts, and fumes cannot be maintained below permissible exposure levels (PELs), welders should wear respiratory protective equipment designated by the National Institute of Occupational Safety and Health (NIOSH).

Clothing Preferences

Welders should cover all parts of their bodies to protect against ultraviolet and infrared ray flash burn. Dark clothing works best to reduce reflection under the face shield.

Wool, leather, or cotton treated to reduce flammability are preferred for welding. Clothing should be thick enough to prevent flash-through burns, be clean, and be free of oil or grease. Clothes should have sleeves and collars buttoned and should have no front pockets that could catch sparks. Welders should wear pants without cuffs. Pants legs should cover the tops of shoes or boots.

If worn, thermal insulated underwear should be covered by other clothing and not exposed to sparks or other ignition sources. It should be down-filled or waffle weave cotton or wool. Quilted nylon-shell/polyester-filled underwear and synthetic outer wear won't necessarily ignite more easily than cotton, but it melts as it burns, sticking tightly to skin, which can result in a very serious burn that is hard to treat and slow to heal.

Housekeeping Is a Priority

Keeping welding areas free of combustibles is extremely important in avoiding fires. Collect used electrodes or rod stubs for safe disposal. Proper storage of compressed gas cylinders is also an element of fire prevention. As always, store tools in the appropriate place.

Work at Working Safely

In all welding operations, take time to evaluate the job and implement appropriate safety precautions. This step will not only prevent equipment and machine damage, but it will reduce the risk of an accident that could injure you or a co-worker.

NOTES

Employee _____

Instructor _____

Date _____

Location _____

WELDING REVIEW

1. Welding fumes:
   a. Are hot enough to melt steel.
   b. Are composed of microscopic particles.
   c. Can cause fires.
   d. Are harmless.

2. _____ is a basic type of welding operation:
   a. Arc flash.
   b. Resistance.
   c. Oxygen-argon gas.
   d. All of the above.

3. Common welding hazards can include:
   a. Microwave and ultraviolet radiation can damage the eyes.
   b. Vapors and mists are poisonous.
   c. Welding on closed containers can cause them to explode.
   d. None of the above.

4. Oxygen cylinders:
   a. Are supposed to leak a little.
   b. Can be dangerous if the gauges or regulators are broken.
   c. Normally show burn marks after the first time they're used.
   d. All of the above.

5. An example of a compressed gas that can easily catch fire and burn is:
   a. Propane.
   b. Nitrogen.
   c. Argon.
   d. Carbon dioxide.

6. If you weld in an elevated area:
   a. You don't need fall protection such as a guardrail.
   b. Be sure to protect employees who might be below you.
   c. You don't need to put up a warning sign for hot surfaces when you're done.
   d. It's safer to do resistance welding if the surface is wet.

7. When handling an oxygen compressed gas cylinder:
   a. Wear oily gloves.
   b. Be absolutely certain it arrived in the horizontal position.
   c. Be sure to grease the valve before you open it.
   d. Identify its dangers by looking at the safety data sheet before you use it.

8. When you open the valve on a compressed gas cylinder:
   a. Make sure there's gas building up pressure in the regulator.
   b. Open the valve as quickly as you can.
   c. Point the outlet away from people and sources of ignition.
   d. Use any type of wrench to open a valve with hand wheels.

9. If you see a cylinder marked with "MT" it means:
   a. The cylinder is empty.
   b. The cylinder was manufactured in Montana.
   c. The cylinder contains a "monoatomic" gas.
   d. The cylinder needs to be inspected and recertified.

10. Have a hot work permit:
    a. To ensure fire hazards are under control when you weld.
    b. If the object to be welded can't be moved to a safe area.
    c. If all of the fire hazards in the area can't be moved to a safe area.
    d. All of the above.

WORKPLACE SECURITY

In the past, security personnel were concerned with things like the theft of the facility's equipment or computer hackers breaking through the computer system's firewall and planting computer viruses. While these types of crimes are still a concern, employers have new security risks to deal with these days.

What Are the Risks?

Security breaches can result in threats, violence, injury, illness, property loss, or business shut-downs.

In order to keep employees, clients, and visitors safe, employers and employees must be alert for various types of serious security risks:

- Penetration of secure areas.

- Assaults.

- Theft of hazardous materials or other property.

- Chemical and biological terrorism.

- Misuse of classified materials.

Start With Parking Lot and Garage Security

When you enter an employee parking lot or garage, remember to think of your own personal security and safety. While there is no one criteria for determining "safe" parking spots, try to park:

- Where you can see for a distance around your vehicle.

- Where you can be seen (a highly visible location).

- In busy areas of the lot, close to the building entrance or public walkways, if possible.

Often, an organization will issue parking stickers. Frequently, parking spaces are marked for employee- or visitor-only use. These procedures help to identify employees and persons who may not belong in the facility. Whenever you witness suspicious activity in a parking lot or garage, or if you notice a vehicle that is out of place or appears abandoned, promptly report it to security personnel.

Parking Lots

Outdoor, ground-level parking lots are safer if they are:

- Well-lit and highly-visible.

- Fenced to limit access (fenced, gated, and guarded if necessary).

- Patrolled, especially at night.

Parking Garages

If you park in a multi-level parking garage, you face risks that are different from parking in an open ground-level parking lot. The columns used to hold up the parking garage roof limit visibility. The artificial lighting in these structures is normally not as good as daylight, and vandals can break or disconnect the light bulbs.

In addition, parking garages usually have secluded stairwells where assaults often occur. Elevators pose the same types of risks.

Going to and From Your Vehicle

Before you get out of your locked automobile, scan the area around the vehicle. Are there any suspicious people in the immediate area? If so, move to another parking spot.

When you exit your vehicle:

- Quickly move toward the building entrance, scanning the area in front of you for suspicious people and behavior.

- Walk in well-lit areas.

- Stay alert, and if a suspicious person does approach, change directions and head for a safe area.

- Use a security alarm if you are threatened.

When you leave the building and return to your vehicle:

- Ask for a security escort if this service is available.

- Scan the area around your vehicle as you approach.

- Approach your vehicle with care; have your keys ready.

- If something appears out of the ordinary, or if you see a suspicious person approaching; stop, and go back into the building or other safe area. Contact security or call the police.

Maintain Secure Entrances

One way to protect a building is to make it difficult to get close to it. This is often accomplished by a fence or wall.

Fences should be hard to climb over or to penetrate, and they could be supplemented with security cameras to make them even more effective.

Many workplaces now operate controlled access entrances. These are usually security checkpoints that are manned or unmanned. That means that there may be a:

- Security person or receptionist at the gate or door to screen the people entering the grounds or building.

- Device that automatically scans employee identification (ID) cards or badges. Without a valid ID, the door or gate will not open.

Security cameras are often used to provide surveillance around building entrances. Often the mere sight of a security camera will deter criminals. Of course, these cameras have to be monitored by a receptionist or security person.

Security Measures Inside the Facility

Just because you've made it safely inside the workplace, you shouldn't let your guard down. If your organization has relatively few employees, you may know everyone who works there. But, your workplace may be just too large and spread out for employees to be able to recognize everyone who is authorized to be inside. Or, your business may work with the public or other clients who come and go throughout the day.

Watch for people or other employees:

- Attempting to access something that is normally denied them, such as: classified materials, chemicals, hazardous materials, or admission to prohibited or secure areas.

- Behaving in a strange manner.

- Making unusual requests or demands.

- Carrying a weapon (unless they are authorized to do so).

Report suspicious activities to the facility's security office.

Can We See Some Identification?

One security measure that is often overlooked is proper identification for employees. Some organizations require employees to wear identification badges or carry identification cards. The most effective IDs have the employee's picture, along with his or her name and department, on the badge. This is the most effective way to determine if the person belongs in the building. It also is good deterrent to the theft of the ID.

Never allow just anyone into your workplace. It is good policy to require each employee to use his or her own ID to enter the building.

While requiring the use of an ID badge to enter the property increases security, the scanning device cannot tell if the person with the badge is the same person the badge was issued to. In other words, a stolen employee security card will allow anyone to enter the building. Make sure that you know where your security card is at all times. If your card is lost or stolen, immediately report this to your security office.

Visitor Security

Visitors to your workplace should be required to register at an entrance location before they move about your facility. The employee they have come to visit should meet them at this secure location.

After security personnel have verified that the visitors are to be allowed into your workplace, they should be required to wear some form of identification. These visitors should be restricted to traveling with the employee they have come to see and should not be allowed to wander off alone.

Outside maintenance or construction personnel working at your facility should also be screened, registered, and required to wear an identification badge.

After the meeting has taken place or the work has been completed, make sure visitors and contractors return the ID badges, and indicate on the record that they have left the building.

If the public has access to your workplace, limit the areas they can enter. Provide employees with ID cards or keys that will allow them to enter secured areas that are locked to the public.

Mail Room Security

Employees in the mail room are at risk of being directly exposed to threats from outside of your organization. Mail room employees need to know how to recognize potential threats and take extra precautions.

The Federal Bureau of Investigation (FBI) has issued an advisory detailing what you should do if you receive a suspicious letter or package:

1. Handle with care. Do not shake or bump the item.

2. Isolate and look for indicators:

   - No return address.

   - Restrictive marking such as "PERSONAL."

   - Excessive postage (could have been mailed from a foreign country).

   - Misspelled words.

   - Bad handwriting or typing.

   - Wrong title with name.

   - Addresses to a title only or an incorrect title.

   - Protruding wires.

   - Item is lopsided or uneven.

   - A strange odor.

   - Oily stains, discolorations, or crystallization on wrapper.

   - Excessive tape or string.

If a parcel is open and/or a threat is identified:

1. For a bomb:

   - Evacuate immediately.

   - Call Police (911).

   - Contact the local FBI office.

2. For a radiological threat:
   - Limit exposure to the item and don't handle it.
   - Evacuate the area.
   - Shield yourself from the object.
   - Call Police (911).
   - Contact the local FBI office.

3. For a biological or chemical threat:
   - Isolate the item and don't handle it.
   - Call Police (911).
   - Wash your hands with soap and warm water.
   - Contact the local FBI office.

Work at Working Safely

Having some fear is normal and helps people remain vigilant, but there are many precautions both employers and employees can take to help ensure a secure workplace where risks are reduced.

1. Take personal safety and security precautions in parking lots and garages.

2. Follow all secure entry policies and procedures.

3. Report suspicious activities in the workplace.

4. Always wear or carry your ID in the workplace.

5. Report lost or stolen employee ID badges.

6. Make sure visitors check in and out when they are allowed in your facility.

7. Limit public access to your workplace.

8. Know what actions to take if you receive a suspicious package.

Safe at Home

Your home is your castle, so take precautions to keep your valuables safe from intruders. Home security goes beyond making sure you keep your doors locked. You can certainly follow many of the safety tips described in this chapter when you aren't at work, but also consider:

- Having adequate insurance coverage.

- Keeping an inventory of your belongings, including records of serial numbers. Use photos or videos to help document your possessions.

- Renting a safe deposit box, or installing a home safe.

- Making sure all of your family members know how to report suspicious activity to the police.

Employee _____

Instructor _____

Date _____

Location _____

WORKPLACE SECURITY REVIEW

1. To improve your personal security in a parking lot:
   a. Try to hide your car in a dark area.
   b. Park in spaces reserved for handicapped drivers.
   c. Park away from the building entrance to get some exercise.
   d. Park where you can see for a distance around your vehicle.

2. Report to security personnel if you see:
   a. A vehicle with a company parking sticker in an employee spot.
   b. A vehicle without a company parking sticker parked in a visitor spot.
   c. A vehicle that looks abandoned in the far end of the lot.
   d. None of the above.

3. Risks in parking garages can include:
   a. Secluded stairwells and elevators.
   b. Dim lighting.
   c. Columns and walls that limit visibility.
   d. All of the above.

4. When you return to the parking lot:
   a. Don't get out your keys until you're at your vehicle.
   b. Go back into the building or to a safe area if a suspicious person approaches.
   c. Look straight ahead, directly at your vehicle, as you approach it.
   d. Don't trust anyone who appears to be the security escort.

5. Security features for a building's entrance area include all of the following except:
   a. Fences.
   b. Cameras.
   c. A receptionist to screen people who enter.
   d. Poor lighting and shrubs that create hiding spots.

6. Security cameras:
   a. Are only effective if they're located in the parking lot.
   b. Are often used around building entrances.
   c. Are only effective if no one can notice them.
   d. Do not need to be monitored.

7. When you can't recognize everyone in the workplace, suspect someone who:
   a. Is trying to access a prohibited area.
   b. Is making unusual requests.
   c. Is behaving strangely, such as loitering near a hazardous material storage area.
   d. All of the above.

8. A lost or stolen security badge:
   a. Isn't any security threat.
   b. Could be used by someone else to enter the building.
   c. Shouldn't be reported until it's been missing at least a week.
   d. None of the above.

9. Visitors:
   a. Never pose a security risk.
   b. Should be required to register.
   c. Are the people who aren't wearing any identification.
   d. Shouldn't have an employee escort.

10. Suspicious letters or packages:
    a. Should be isolated from other items.
    b. Shouldn't be shaken or dropped.
    c. Should be reported to the police.
    d. All of the above.